THE COMMONSENSE BOOK OF DRINKING

Also by LEON D. ADAMS

THE COMMONSENSE BOOK OF WINE

The Commonsense Book of Drinking

BY LEON D. ADAMS

With a Foreword by
MORRIS FISHBEIN, M.D.

DAVID McKAY COMPANY, INC.
New York

Library of Congress Catalogue Card Number: 60-7113

MANUFACTURED IN THE UNITED STATES OF AMERICA

VAN REES PRESS • NEW YORK

Second Printing, November 1960

To JERRY AND BRIAN

Foreword

From the time when I was very young I observed the drinking of wine in our family home as a part of the Jewish ritual of living. In the 1890's, when I was about seven years old, a kindly aunt, who would forbid me nothing, supplied my request for a glass of beer because all the rest of the family were drinking beer at dinner. I became dreadfully sick, and as a result no doubt of the psychological effects I did not begin to enjoy beer again until I went to Europe in 1931.

When I entered the university, students drank but seldom to the point of intoxication. Only twice in my life have I been inebriated and both times were in the university—once on apricot brandy and the second time on champagne. Incidentally, it is hard for me to get inebriated on champagne.

In all the years of my maturity I have never hesitated to take alcohol in a variety of forms whenever I wanted and that means in great moderation. In fact, many of my best friends who ask always for double or triple Martinis or double scotches on the rocks usually preface their invitation to me by saying, "You don't drink, do you?"

I am moved to these reminiscences by reading and enjoying every page of Leon Adams' *The Commonsense Book of Drinking*. A famous poet once characterized tea as the drink that cheers but not inebriates. Of a great many alcoholic beverages one could say that they frequently cheer but only inebriate when taken to immoderate excess.

About the age of nineteen I saw my first case of delirium tremens. Perhaps it impressed me so much that it governed my imbibing ever after. Perhaps moderation could be taught by exposing the adolescent mind to observation of cases of the d.t.'s. This reminds me that we still need much research on the effects of alcohol and of various types of alcoholic beverages on the human body. As one learns from Mr. Adams' fine presentation, even the effects of alcohol are frequently conditioned by mental factors. No doubt all chronic alcoholics have a mental problem that is far more important than any physical difficulty from which they suffer.

This book contains an amazing amount of information which has been collected with meticulous care from a wide variety of sources. Bartenders have been interviewed as well as the scientists associated with universities and research institutes. One myth after another is exploded by the citation of facts. One learns how the words "gin," "whisky," "proof," and "brandy" originated. The innovation of vodka is analyzed. An extensive chapter tells the facts about beer and again dismisses the peculiar legends that have attached themselves to this family beverage. The chapters are full of excellent aphorisms. Among the best is "Nothing—absolutely nothing—cures a hangover, except time."

If I keep on with this foreword I will make it longer than the book, but if it encourages reading of the book by those who are interested—and everyone should be—I will be happy for having written it, even if I did not count Leon Adams among my friends.

MORRIS FISHBEIN, M.D.

Chicago, Illinois
February 1960

Author's Note

SEVERAL MONTHS BEFORE THE RESEARCH FOR THIS BOOK WAS completed, I was addressing a local luncheon club about my earlier book on wine. During the question-and-answer period a member of the audience asked what the title of my next book would be. When I replied that it would be *The Commonsense Book of Drinking,* there was a moment of silence. Then a voice came from the rear: "So now you've started writing fiction!"

There was some laughter. After the meeting my heckler stopped by to expound. "You're wasting your time," he said. "People don't want to drink with common sense. Nobody who guzzles liquor wants to know why or how."

I replied that I write only the things millions of Americans want to know about drinks and drinking in relation to themselves as imbibers, hosts, hostesses, parents, or citizens. Most of what is generally "known" on these subjects simply isn't true, I said, and some simple facts are urgently needed.

"Well, maybe that kind of book *is* needed," my heckler conceded, "but it can't be common sense. That term implies freedom from bias. Everybody is biased, one way or another, about drinking. I am, and so are you."

He was right, of course. I am biased for freedom of the individual to do, eat, or drink whatever he chooses—so long as he does not thereby harm or greatly annoy others.

This book is neither a defense nor an apology for drinking. It is an attempt to explain some things about it.

Emphatically it is not written for problem drinkers, who are becoming recognized nowadays as sick people. Their only cure is total abstinence. It is written for the great majority of people who can take alcoholic beverages or leave them alone.

I have enjoyed beer, wine, liquor, and cordials temperately since childhood. In my early youth, shocked by public drunkenness in my neighborhood, I thought prohibition, then not yet enacted nationally, an excellent idea. Later, as a young newspaperman covering the prohibition beat during the Volstead era, I saw that it obviously was not. Since then I have crusaded for the sensible use of beverage alcohol, especially in the form of wine taken with meals, in the United States.

The bookstores and libraries of America are plentifully supplied with excellent hosts' handbooks, useful bartending guides, frightening scientific tomes about alcohol in the human system, romantic odes to individual beverages, volumes that violently condemn all drinking and others that stoutly defend it. There also are some flippant, slangy pieces that take a tolerant view of hilarious binges, comical drunks, and headachy mornings after. No single volume thus far has attempted to supply—uncluttered by footnotes, references, ecstatic praise, or emotional diatribes—all of the important facts that most sober people need or would like to have about the various drinks available and what each kind of potion does to or for the individual when it is swallowed. The need has been for someone to compile and write a sober drinker's handbook, a guide to sober drinking for the forgotten man—the vast majority who use alcoholic beverages without creating problems for themselves or others and who have been ignored by scientific writers because all of the emphasis today is on problem drinkers.

This book is a reporter's conscientious attempt to do so fully, accurately, and frankly.

Why a reporter? Why not an alcohol researcher, a distiller, a brewer, or a vintner? Because there is such wide divergence of views among such authorities that no one of them in any branch of his given field can represent the conflicting judgments of his colleagues. To summarize and relate objectively what is known or contended in these fields is, therefore, a task of reporting.

For accuracy I have verified many of the more controversial portions of text by personally submitting them to the acknowledged leading authorities on the points at issue, for discussion and in some instances for correction.

Some of the brewers, vintners, and distillers will disapprove of what I have written. I suspect they will react as some winegrowers have reacted to my *Commonsense Book of Wine,* not denying the truth of the things I tell, but complaining: "Why did you have to tell people *that?*" Eventually, I think, the honest makers and purveyors of alcoholic beverages will be more benefited than harmed by wide dissemination of important truths about their merchandise, even though their advertisements are thereby contradicted.

Perhaps certain researchers, whose theories I have tried to summarize impartially, will object to what they may regard as my oversimplification of their findings. This is unavoidable in a book intended for lay readers. Also some of the things that I state as facts, based on the results of research available at this writing, will surely be contradicted or modified by other research in the future; this occurs frequently in all fields of science. I can only hope that I have distilled at least some clear information from the floods of scientific data that have been produced in recent years by the host of professionally expert seekers after facts in the weird world of the drug, alcohol.

I am deeply grateful to the many individual experts who have answered my questions frankly, but I shall not attempt to name them because most were promised anonymity. The hundreds of books, pamphlets, and other encyclopedic publications from which data have been extracted would make far too long a list to be reproduced here. I also thank the several of my neighbors who have reviewed the text for clarity, and whose suggestions have improved it appreciably.

LEON D. ADAMS

Contents

FOREWORD By Morris Fishbein, M.D. v

AUTHOR'S NOTE vii

1. YOU AND YOUR DRINKING 3

Doesn't Everybody?—Why Imbibe at All—Better than Pills—Least Harmful Narcotic—Loosen Tight Nerves—The Social Lubricant—Your Kind of Tippler

2. WHAT BARTENDERS KNOW 10

Secrets of Cautious Drinking—Eat When You Drink—Call for "A Tall One"—Water Your Martinis—Must You Never "Mix" Your Drinks?—Tranquilizers and Liquor—Bargains in Bars—Which Servings Are Stingy—They Learn About People—What Bartenders *Don't* Know

3. IT GETS IN YOUR BLOOD 14

The Food You Don't Digest—A Startling Experiment—Your Hard-Working Liver—The Why of Red Noses—Anesthetic and Wonder Drug—Easiest with a Needle—Your Body Must Burn It—Gay, Tipsy, or Bleary

4. HOW MUCH CAN YOU HOLD? 18

Know Your A.Q. (Alcohol Quotient)—Measure the Dose—Your Body Weight Figures—How Many, How Strong, How Fast—How Soon Are You Sober?—Lining Your Stomach—When Servings Vary—How Much Total Alcohol—Ten Beers at a Sitting?—When Can You Drive?—Why Martinis Are Deadly—Other Drinks Rated—Some Kinds Are Slower—Folks with Hollow Legs—Does Your Capacity Increase?—Those Who Can't Hold Any—When You're Tired, Tense, or Happy—The Dose That Can Kill—Drinkometer—Sobering-up Time

5. SPIRITS ARE STRONGEST 32

Why They're so Potent—New Spirits Are Colorless—Diluted with Water—Are There Bargains in Liquor?—How Much Is Tax—What Some Labels Mean—How Moonshiners Cheat—Bootleggers' Secrets—Legal White Lightning—Strange Story of "Proof"

6. WHISKEYS UNSCRAMBLED 40

What's a "Good" Whiskey?—The Seven Whiskey Flavors—Smoke in Your Scotch—You Only *Think* You Drink Rye—Which "Burns More" Going Down?—Those "Neutral Spirits"—What Canadians Don't Tell—Weird World of Whiskey—St. Patrick and Irish Whiskey—How Bourbon Was Born—Sour Mash Is Sweet—"Bond" Means Look Out!—When There's Wine in Your Whiskey—How Liquors Are Changing—Myth of Great Age

7. GIN, VODKA, RUM, AND THE REST 54

Gin Was Genièvre—What Hits You Fastest—"Dead Drunk for Twopence"—Brandy for Gentlemen—Armagnac and Grappa—"Blackberry Brandy" Isn't—Rum from Molasses—The Most Powerful Kind—Is Vodka Just Alcohol?—You Can Buy the Real Stuff—Aquavit, Tequila, and "Oke"

8. HIGHBALLS, COCKTAILS, SHOTS, AND ELIXIRS 72

The Long and the Short of It—To Stay off the Rocks—Do Bubbles Intoxicate?—Don't Drink Scotch Cows—The Kinds You Buy Bottled—The Original Martini—Measure Your Liquor—Exotic Elixirs—Cordials Are Liqueurs—Some Make Them at Home—Why France Banished Absinthe—What about Lunchtime Cocktails?

9. BEER BENIGN 84

Lager Means Aged—Ales Are Hoppier—"Malt Liquors" Are Strongest—Can Beer Intoxicate?—What Labels Seldom Tell You—Beer as a Tranquilizer—What's Happened to Flavor?—They're Blaming Women—Are Today's Beers Better?—Some Prefer Near-Beer—Can You Tell the Difference?—Brewsters Were Ladies—Return of Home Brew—There's Flavor in Foam—How to Wash Glasses—Why Salt in Your Beer?—Is "On Draught" Really Different?—The Fresher the Better—Best Bargains in Beer—Tap Brew for Picnics—Other Kinds Described—Mead from Honey—Cactus Juice Makes Pulque

10. THE WISDOM OF WINE 108

It's Only Something to Drink—Connoisseur Lore Confuses—Are Imported Wines Better?—Battle about Names—What "Dry" Really Means—Most Are Best Young—Kinds that Improve with Age—What "Vintage" Means—Bargains in Wine—Most Relaxing of All Beverages—Claret for Boys, Port for Men—What's the Truth About France?—Italy, Sobriety, and Russia

11. FACTS AND FABLES 124

A Matter of Dilution—Some Popular Myths Exploded—Does a Drink Make You Sleepy?—Stimulants and Anesthetics—Don't Depend on Coffee—Are There Love Potions?—Drinking While Pregnant—Are All Drinks Alike?—The Ones that Creep Up—What Does a Chaser Do?—Bitters Are Appetizers—Some Are Allergic—What Makes You Sick—Hiccups Are Spasms—Does Smoking Make a Difference?—Must Your Breath Tell?—Can They Warm or Cool You?—Drinking While Flying—Colds, Heart Trouble, and Ulcers—When Drinks Are Forbidden—Alcoholics Are Undernourished—Are Offspring Affected?—What Causes Problem Drinking?—They Get Drunk on Water—Prize Fable from Moscow

12. TRUTH ABOUT HANGOVER 143

A Question of Chemistry—What Makes Them Thirsty—Hungover without Drinking—Remorse Makes It Worse—"Must Have Been Sleep That Did It"—Cures that Won't Work—"Hair of the Dog"—Can It Be Prevented?—Scotch and Champagne Hangovers—Strange Story of Congeners

13. FOR WISE HOSTS AND GUESTS 150

Case of the Nondrinking Hosts—How to Save Your Furniture—The Gadget to Buy—Never Slug Your Guests' Drinks—High Protein Tidbits—Bibulous Late Arrivals—Something for Those on the Wagon—How Long Before Dinner?—Glamour vs. Strength—Guarding Your Budget—Problem of the Wedding Reception—Minimum Home Assortments—Businessman's Dilemma—Beware of Home Bartenders—How to Nurse a Drink

14. HOW TO DRINK AND STAY THIN 157

Stage and Screen People Do It—A Matter of Arithmetic—Balanced Diet Is Vital—Why Alcohol Is Fattening—Which

Drinks Affect Appetite—Raiding the Refrigerator—Avoid Sweet Mixers—Drinks with Long Sipping-Time—Lower Proof, Fewer Calories—Drink-Calorie Table

15. LIQUOR FOR CHILDREN 163

What Youngsters Are Drinking—Some Have Parents' Permission—"They Call You 'Chicken' "—Some Try to Prove They're Men—Lure of the Forbidden—The Fear That Won't Prevent—Irish, Italians, Jews—"We Teach Them Everything Else"—Do They Remember Their First Drink?

16. WARNINGS OF DANGER 170

What Most People Want to Know—Some Should Never Drink—The Five Danger Signals—Is Alcoholism a Disease?—How *Not* to Treat a Problem Drinker

17. A PLEA FOR SANITY 174

Laws that Fail—Those "Monopoly" States—Election Day Drinking—Strange Minimum Age Laws—The Mississippi Story—Liquor Tax on Water—What's Moral, Anyhow?—Drip-Dry States—We're Still Fighting Wet-Dry Battles—What's "Community Veto"?—How Prohibition Began—What Churches Are Saying

18. MANNERS FOR DRINKING AMERICA 182

We're Becoming Civilized—Growing Power of Women—Are Cocktail Parties Necessary?—Hip Flasks Are Passé—Lessons from Primitive Cultures—Intolerance of Drunkenness—Power of Ostracism

APPENDIX Guide to Wines, Spirits, and Drink Terms 187

INDEX 201

THE COMMONSENSE BOOK OF DRINKING

CHAPTER 1

You and Your Drinking

WHETHER YOU SIP ALCOHOLIC LIQUORS, SWIG THEM, OR SHUN them as concoctions of the devil, they are part of your life. You live in a society where two out of three adults regularly consume beverages containing ethyl alcohol and where drinks and drinking rank with diet and sex as leading topics of conversation. If you buy and serve beer, wine, or liquor, they affect both your budget and your status as a host. If you drink any of them, the alcohol gets into your blood stream.

There are some things you should know about them, and many of the facts in these pages will surprise you.

Most people wonder about the various kinds of drinks and about themselves and drinking. They continually ask such questions as these, and any answers they get are oftener wrong than right: "Is it safe to drink beer after whiskey?" "What liquor should I buy for a cocktail party?" "Why does wine make me sleepy?" "Does the best beer have the smallest bubbles?" "Does Scotch creep up on you faster than bourbon?" "How much alcohol does ale contain?" "Which is better—straight whiskey or blend?" "Must I breast-feed my baby to keep him from growing up a drunkard?" "How can I drink with my customers and still stay sober?" To supply commonsense answers to these and hundreds of other such questions is the purpose of this book.

Significantly, the oftenest-asked question is: "When am I in danger of becoming an alcoholic?" This one crops up so regularly that an entire later chapter is devoted to the answer.

I have a salesman friend whose dinner is usually preceded by two double Martinis and his breakfast by Bromo-Seltzer. Discussing with me one evening my researches on beer and liquor, he said: "Wherever I go, on business or on friendly visits, I'm expected to bend elbows with someone. Doesn't it seem to you, as it does to me, that just about everybody drinks too much nowadays?"

For him and for others who move in overly convivial circles the answer is that at least sixty-five million adult Americans use alcoholic beverages with seldom if ever a morning-after headache, that five million often drink to excess, that one million are addicts who depend upon liquor to be happy, and that no fewer than thirty-five million men and women in the United States are unswerving teetotalers, whose number is steadily increasing.

Lifelong abstainers have the best longevity records. Although it has also been claimed that moderate drinkers live just as long (and some defenders of alcohol argue that nondrinkers include many nonsmokers and careful dieters), this fact stands out: Your body does not require beverage alcohol to be healthy.

On the other hand, here are some facts that will shock any readers who happen to be prohibitionists. Your blood at all times contains approximately .003 per cent alcohol. Nursing mothers' milk and the bread you eat are slightly alcoholic, too. The vanilla and almond extracts on your pantry shelf contain 35 per cent alcohol; the labels say so. Many cough remedies and other liquid patent medicines, including a famous preparation for female disorders, are considerably more intoxicating than beer, ale, or the average wine. One reason some iron-rich tonics make you feel good is the alcohol they contain. Certain after-shave and hair lotions are so alcoholic that their sales skyrocket whenever liquor goes up in price or becomes hard to obtain.

Nowadays even your beefsteak, lamb chops, cheese, and milk probably come from animals that are lapping up the new liquid livestock feeds that contain 10 per cent alcohol—almost as much as the average highball. The livestock (partly because the alcohol can't get past their multiple stomachs) do not get drunk, but they love the stuff anyhow, and produce better meat.

There are several kinds of alcohol, but the one we are considering is ethanol (chemically speaking, C_2H_5OH), a clear, colorless, inflammable, volatile liquid which is essentially tasteless but produces a hot, burning sensation in your mouth. You can run your car or clean grease from your clothes with it. It is contained, in varying proportions, in beer, ale, porter, stout, wine, mead, aquavit, vodka, whiskey, rum, brandy, cordials, and all of the other beverages this book undertakes to unscramble. Alcohol is everywhere—in foods, medicines, mouth washes, antiseptics, perfumes, tobacco, fuels, paints, antifreeze, to mention only a few of its thousand uses.

But why in the name of common sense do we drink it?

The history of the human race supplies the best of all answers: It is part of the nature of mankind. One of the first differences between man and his simian ancestors is that man, wherever he has found himself, has always managed to get or make something alcoholic to drink.

Columbus found the Caribbean Indians drinking beer brewed of maize by their women. The Incas of Peru made wine and beer before Pizarro came. Magellan arrived in the Philippines to find the natives drinking the fermented sap of the coconut palm, a potation still made there, and with paralyzing qualities to which American servicemen can eloquently testify. In Abyssinia there is bouza, a kind of beer to which powdered leaves of the geshu plant are added to make it more than mildly intoxicating and from which the English term "booze" may well have originated, although Webster says the word is European. Tartar tribesmen make an intoxicating drink from the milk of mares and camels fermented with rennet. The Laplanders ferment reindeer milk into a dizzying liquid called pima. Natives on some South Sea Islands chew and ferment the intoxicating pepper plant to make kava, choko, or namoluk, which paralyzes the legs while the head remains clear. Mexico has had its pulque, the fermented juice of maguey cactus, since the Mayan era; India its palm wine or toddy. Mead was fermented from honey in Britain long before the Romans came. Indians in British Columbia now buy a can of tomatoes and a cake of yeast and get drunk on the fermented result. In New Mexico grows the cactus called whiskey plant, whose fruit the Indians eat for the effect the name implies. The early Chinese fermented the flesh of lambs in milk and then distilled it into *kau-yang-tsyew,* the favorite drink of their emperors.

The word "symposium" originally meant, among the ancient Greeks, a drinking party. Explorers in Borneo found the aboriginal Dyak headhunters had long been making beer out of rice. During World War II as much 190-proof torpedo juice was drunk by sailors as was used to fire "tin fish." Convicts in our prisons, denied spiritus frumenti, sniff benzedrine and paint thinner for kicks, drink duplicator fluid, hoard raisins and prunes and ferment them into wine, and they even fashion ingenious distilling apparatus to manufacture moonshine behind the walls.

As for the Mohammedans, abjured in the Koran to avoid wine as the work of Satan, "who seeketh to sow dissension and hatred" among them, they, too, have always had their alcohol and their share of problem drinkers. The more liberal Moslems drink wine and beer openly; and even in Saudi Arabia, where the Prophet's word is taken literally, and beards abound, the sale of shaving lotion is remarkably high.

We of the twentieth-century Western world imbibe for a variety of motives. In his famed textbook of neurology S. A. Kinnier-Wilson stated a few of them: "Some people use alcohol because they like the taste, others because they enjoy its exhilarating effect, others because they want to drown their sorrows, and still others because they want to get drunk."

His list is incomplete. He omitted relaxation, relief from tension, and feelings of calmness and self-importance. Alcohol, the least harmful of narcotics, taken in moderate doses, furnishes all of these better than any of the tranquilizing pills can, and with considerably less danger, which is why doctors often prescribe it. He also neglected to mention sociability and sin—the latter two being strangely related.

There is no more efficient social lubricant, no simpler way to establish rapport with your fellow man, than to drink with him, and it cannot be done with soda pop. This fact is somehow involved with the faint guilt feeling most Americans sense every time they take liquid cheer—that they are getting away with a minor sin. Drinking together is something like sinning together. The perversity of man lends fascination to that which is dangerous or forbidden. Nobody has expressed this better than Hugh Garrecht, president of the Milk

Industry Foundation, who once said: "We could sell a lot more of our product if we could find a way to make milk drinking sinful."

Let us now brush aside this aura of sin, and the horrors, myths, and excuses that surround and distort the truth about drinking. Let us become bluntly personal.

If you do not use any alcoholic beverage—and this book does not advocate that you should or should not—you ought to know these things because what other people do affects your welfare. If you are the average reader, who does imbibe, let us consider your kind of tippler. You are assumed to be one of the "moderate" drinkers.

To qualify as "moderate" means that you savor the taste of what you drink, that you choose your beverage for its flavor, not for its strength; that such physiological and psychological effects as the feelings of relaxation and conviviality you get are usually a secondary, not your only, reason for drinking; that you do not seek to be drunk, but avoid it; and that these beverages are neither a necessity for you nor a considerable item in your personal budget.

Primitive, childish man had no connoisseur bent; he drank not to enjoy the flavor of his liquor, but solely to get drunk. He always has, and he still does.

In other words, it is not what you drink, but why, that is important.

Assuming, then, that "moderate" describes your drinking, you are the person for whom this book is mainly intended. You want to know many things—what happens when you drink; what is really behind the mysterious labels on the rows of bottles that confront you in the stores, bars, restaurants, and homes of America; how their contents taste; why their flavors have lately been changing; how to choose among them, and how each would behave if you poured it into your system.

These things will be told, many little-known facets of drinks and drinking will be explored, and a great deal of fog and superstition may be dispelled in the chapters that follow.

CHAPTER 2

What Bartenders Know

TO BEGIN BRUSHING AWAY THE COBWEBS THAT OBSCURE IMPORtant truths about drinks and drinking, the first man we shall consult is the professional bartender. I have quizzed him in many places, from the plushy clubs where wealthy people tipple to the seamiest dives where even the determined researcher ventures with qualms. Practicing amateur psychiatry along with his mixology, the man behind the bar learns much that could enlighten all who buy, use, or serve the stuff he dispenses. Although he lacks clinical training, and therefore misconstrues some things and imagines others, there are several things he knows better than any scientific observer does.

For one thing, he knows secrets of cautious drinking. He can tell you to eat while you drink, or, better yet, before you take even a sip. He knows that the "kick" a given drink delivers depends upon whether there is food in your stomach before the liquor gets there. The lesson of putting drinks into an empty stomach, when learned by trial and error, often leads to traumatic experiences. This is one reason why the best bars serve potato chips, peanuts, popcorn, and oily hors d'oeuvres for no extra charge at cocktail time.

Get a bartender's confidence and he'll admit that the proprietor has another, less altruistic motive for providing these snacks: patrons who partake of them feel their liquor less, the salt makes them thirsty, and he sells them more drinks.

Dilute your liquor, he can also advise you. When ordering a highball in a tavern, call for "a tall one," which means in barroom parlance serving the same amount of liquor in a ten-ounce glass instead of the customary seven-ounce tumbler. This doubles the quantity of diluting water or mix; you take the alcohol more slowly; the barb is blunted; you get the lift without the wallop.

At home the same advice holds; when preparing Martinis, stir them briskly with plenty of ice, thus watering the gin as the barkeep does. In homes, as in bars, people govern only the *number* of drinks they take, regardless of how potent the host has made them. Bars protect their patrons, as well as their profits, by measuring liquor quantities carefully. The considerate home bartender should do likewise.

Actually, the professional has the highest respect for the occasional customer who still orders his Martini made the old-fashioned way—two to one—instead of the straight 90-proof gin with only the whiff of vermouth that most people insist on nowadays. The former is a social drink, the latter an anesthetic.

Nowadays bartenders are also helping to squelch the hoary maxim that you must never "mix" your drinks, that you must always stick to one kind of liquor in an evening. This belief owes its prevalence to many a joyless aftermath of such mixtures as wine after whiskey, Scotch after bourbon, and gin after beer. Let us pause here to urge that this fallacy be laid finally to rest: it is how many drinks, not how many kinds, that count—how much total alcohol taken in how short a time. The same unhappy results follow too much of one kind of liquor as too much of different kinds. It is always the same story, of course, that "the last drink did it"; and the answer is simply that the cup gradually became full and finally ran over.

If clinching proof is needed to explode the old notion, just remember that most cocktails, such as Martinis and Manhattans (gin and whiskey, respectively, with vermouth, a flavored wine), are themselves mixtures.

But still beware, tavern oracles say, of a different kind of mixture—the combination of tranquilizing pills with any kind of liquor. A customer who takes a tranquilizer, then a drink or two, is likely to become so tranquil that he cannot even walk home.

Are there bargains in bars? In some, yes—if you know their merchandise and what to ask for. The average place pours one "bar bourbon," one "bar Scotch," one Canadian whiskey, one gin, one vodka, one dry and one sweet vermouth. The brand and quality of each depend on the status of the bar. Unless you specify otherwise, these are what you get in your drinks. One prestige spot may use, as its "bar" whiskey, a brand that is priced 50 per cent higher in stores than the bar whiskeys you will find elsewhere, yet may charge no more, or only pennies more per drink. But if you do not know this, and call specifically for a drink made with the same expensive liquor, you may be charged as much as a third more—the "call whiskey" price—for it.

You can always impress your companions by ordering a particular brand. But in some smokier bistros, where the top liquor brands are kept on the back bar for mere display, you had better watch to see that you get it. Unwary patrons, ordering their third or fourth drink, have even been served rotgut moonshine. Barmen well know that few average consumers could tell the costliest straight whiskey from the cheapest if the labels were removed, particularly after a couple of drinks.

The best bargains, of course, are the local brands of beer.

Too often, however, these brands are conveniently out of stock, compelling you to order something more expensive.

But almost everywhere, in addition to bargains, if any, there also are overpriced liquors, especially the apéritifs, brandies, and cordials. Some of these, for the miniscule quantities actually served, cost the proprietor no more than his other merchandise. Yet you are likely to pay as much as double the place's highball price for a thimbleful. Worst bargain of all is the average bar's stingy two-ounce serving of inexpensive sherry. Yet tavern keepers sometimes wonder why they don't sell more of this most famous of all cocktail-time wines.

Give up any idea that you can impress a bartender. He is too blasé about people and the problems they relate to him to be impressed by anybody. He can tell a one-drink girl from a four-drink girl and can recognize the high-by-noon drinker at a glance. In fact, he usually knows what you are going to order before you open your mouth—unless it is going to be Scotch and ginger ale, a thought that makes him wince.

What he does not know would fill another book. Ignore, in particular, any barman's prescriptions for hangover preventives or remedies and his opinions about the contents of the miscellaneous bottles brilliantly displayed behind him. These many-shaped flagons are not there simply for show; it is true that each is poured sometimes for someone, but rare is the barman who knows what they all are. Even in places where beer is mainly sold, little is understood about malt beverages. And unless your particular bar is part of a restaurant where a great deal of wine is served with meals daily, believe nothing you may be told about that complex commodity. Few bartenders would know a Cabernet from a Pinot Noir if they both came up and bit him.

CHAPTER 3

It Gets in Your Blood

WHAT HAPPENS WHEN YOU DRINK? PRIMITIVE TRIBESMEN KNOW only that drinking brings them joy, then stupor, which they are prone to credit to gods and demons in their liquors. Modern research has traced alcohol throughout the human system, and has dispelled a great deal of the superstition and mystery that have surrounded the subject for centuries. You now can know exactly how this remarkable drug behaves, step by step, during all of the time it is in your body.

The first thing strong liquor does when it gets past your lips is to irritate your mouth, throat, esophagus, and stomach. This is why topers who take their spirits "neat" develop their whiskey baritone; they have bathed their vocal cords too long in a too concentrated solution of alcohol. They also develop chronic gastritis, the medical term for constant stomach upset. However, beer, wine, and tall highballs, in which the alcohol is well diluted, do not have these effects in the normal human system.

Inside the stomach the drink is diluted by your gastric juices, whose flow is increased by alcohol. But as long as it remains in the stomach, it does not intoxicate; that happens later.

Next comes the thing that makes alcohol different from anything else you take into your system. It is the one kind of food subtance you never digest—the one you feel almost immediately—because it goes directly into your blood. Just where it enters the blood was once a puzzling question to researchers. Some believed it all passes through the stomach wall, which contains tiny blood vessels; and it has been proved that at least a little of it does. Others said the main escape route is through the wall of the small intestine.

A rather startling experiment conducted in a university laboratory finally settled that question. Professors recruited a group of volunteers to do some hard drinking in the name of pure science. There was a catch to the invitation, however: each was required first to let the outlet of his stomach be closed. This was accomplished by tightly strapping to his abdomen a rubber ball that pressed on the pyloric valve (which connects the stomach to the small intestine) with sufficient force to pinch the valve shut. Then each was plied with enough strong liquor to souse thoroughly the average human. Yet every one of the dauntless volunteers remained as sober as the proverbial judge. But when the straps were loosened, wham! all of them soon became quite drunk. Since that classic test there has been no further question about how alcohol gets into the blood.

Once in your veins, further diluted by the blood, it flows to your liver. That remarkable organ begins oxidizing the alcohol. The average liver can handle three quarters of an ounce of 90-proof whiskey or three quarters of a can of beer in an hour. If your liver is average, and if you sip at that poky pace all evening, you will never feel even mildly giddy. But since few ever drink that slowly, most of the alcohol passes through the hard-working liver to the heart, which pumps it to all the organs and tissues of the body.

Its main effect is on the brain and the central nervous system. Its action is narcotic, sedative, relaxing, depressant. It partly anesthetizes the inhibitory centers of the brain, the watchdogs of your body controls and of your conduct. The walls of your skin capillaries relax and are dilated; your heart beats faster, then slower. Blood rushes to the tiny surface blood vessels, increasing perspiration, creating that warm glow, and reddening the face. (This once was blamed for the red noses of some heavy imbibers, but total abstainers, too, display the flaming proboscis, and it no longer is thought to be caused by liquor.)

As the drug bathes the central nervous system, eyesight becomes less keen, accuracy lessens, and muscular coordination is diminished.

But while alcohol is a nerve depressant, it is not a behavior depressant. It blurs pain and care, makes worries of the day fade away, raises confidence and self-esteem, brings to mind pleasant feelings and images, encourages you to do that which your inhibitions, when you are sober, prohibit.

These tranquilizing effects are among the reasons for the wide medical use of alcohol. In its various beverage forms it is often prescribed in the treatment of heart disease, and especially to stimulate the appetite and contribute to the comfort of the aged and the convalescent. It is a quick-energy food, the safest of all sedatives, and one of the most famous of psychological discoveries. Dr. W. Horsley Gantt of John Hopkins University has summed up its therapeutic values in this verbal capsule:

"If alcohol had been discovered only one year ago, instead of in 5000 B.C., it would be the wonder drug of all wonder drugs."

Incidentally, you can also get alcohol into your system by inhaling its fumes, a method which will make you quite dizzy; and some physicians have administered wines rectally. The quickest of all ways to produce intoxication is by injecting alcohol into the vein with a hypodermic needle, but by that route even a small amount, if injected too rapidly, would be instantly fatal.

Once the drug is in your body, how do you get rid of it? The lungs exhale a little—enough to account for that alcoholic breath; and some escapes in perspiration and in urine. The rest—about 90 per cent of the dose—must be burned up by your body, and that takes time. All of your organs and tissues oxidize alcohol to a minor extent, but the liver does most of the job. And this is as good a place as any to emphasize that neither coffee, nor steam baths, nor walks in the cold night air can speed the process one iota. (I hope to convince you of this in a later chapter.)

Remembering, then, that you cannot speed your liver's work, you will see the wisdom of eating before drinking. Food in your stomach keeps the drink in that organ longer, thereby slowing the rate at which the alcohol enters your blood. Diluting your drink, prolonging the time you take to sip it, does the same thing. Both methods help prevent your blood-alcohol level from reaching the peak that brings intoxication. In other words, the amount of alcohol that gets into your blood at any one time determines whether you will be gay, tipsy, or bleary.

CHAPTER 4

How Much Can You Hold?

EVERYBODY KNOWS THAT IN SUNBATHING, SALTING OUR FOOD, indulging in physical exercise, or gulping aspirin, the amount of the dose merits careful measurement. In drinking alcoholic beverages, dosage is no less important.

It is not only the number of drinks and their potency that count, but also the kinds of drinks and the speed at which they are consumed. Moreover, your capacity is not the same as everyone else's. It depends on your body weight, the condition of your system at the moment, and also upon your "A.Q."—your personal Alcohol Quotient—a highly individual statistic that determines when you have had more than you can handle. You may be one of those people who feel a drink after drinking very little; and if so, you had better know it.

Therefore, if you are going to drink at all, you must learn the number of drinks, of what kind, size, and power, that you can take safely under a given set of conditions. But experiment with caution, lest you discover, the hard way, that your A.Q. is lower than average.

But if you are average in all respects, you need not learn entirely by trial and error, for some guideposts are available. That internationally known authority on the arithmetic of inebriation, Dr. Leon A. Greenberg of Yale University, has supplied them.

He has computed that an average adult weighing 150 pounds can drink, without experiencing much more than slight changes in feeling, any of the following: one whiskey highball, or one Old-Fashioned cocktail, or 3½ ounces of sherry, or 6 ounces of table wine, or two bottles of beer. This particular drinker has not had his dinner, and his blood soon acquires, from any one of these five libations, taken within a short time, an alcohol content of .03 per cent.

Double the foregoing dose, and the blood alcohol is also doubled, to .06 per cent. Now the drinker experiences "a feeling of warmth, mental relaxation, a slight decrease of fine skills, less concern with minor irritations and restraints."

Triple it, and the resulting .09 per cent blood-alcohol level brings "buoyancy, exaggerated emotion and behavior." The drinker is "talkative, noisy, or morose."

Quadrupled to .12 per cent, this much causes "impairment of fine coordination, clumsiness, slight to moderate unsteadiness in standing or walking."

A fifth and final dose raises the blood alcohol to .15 per cent—which means "intoxication—unmistakable abnormality of gross bodily functions and mental faculties."

In dose number two—not numbers three, four, or five—you have the basic A.Q. of the average 150-pound man. Now, simple arithmetic tells you that in a person weighing twice as much, the same amount of alcohol should produce only half the concentration in the blood. So look at your bathroom scale and adjust the doses accordingly, up or down, to calculate what theoretically should be your own capacity.

And keep this further point in mind: whether you are tired, starved, sick, tense, angry, relaxed, or happy may make a difference in how drinks affect you, because these things affect your body chemistry in certain ways that we shall explore presently.

But isn't your system burning up some of the alcohol while

these drinks are being taken? The answer is yes, and Dr. Greenberg's figures contain a timetable, too. Each of his highballs, cocktails, or doses of wine or beer takes approximately two hours to disappear from the 150-pound body; it is that simple—four hours for two drinks, six hours for three, eight hours for four, and ten hours for the baneful fifth. Stretch the absorption of the same five highballs uniformly over a period of ten hours, and you may not be drunk at all. Conversely, however, if you drink faster than this rate, your drinks will catch up with you.

Doesn't food in the stomach also prevent intoxication? It helps considerably. Roughly speaking, it takes two drinks after dinner to deliver as much "kick" as one before. Your A.Q. is higher after you have eaten a heavy meal. However, the food only slows the passage of alcohol into your blood. All you have drunk will get there eventually, and it may remind you next morning. The benefits are in lowering the peak effect at any one time and in making the pleasant glow last longer.

You can accomplish much the same thing by lining your stomach in advance with a tablespoonful of olive oil or cream, or a few glasses of milk, or, better yet, high-protein tidbits of egg and meat, which contain certain amino acids. Prudent businessmen, when attending conventions and cocktail parties where they feel compelled to drink, make this a regular practice. So do many Washingtonians who must regularly attend diplomatic receptions, to which they sometimes refer as "capital punishment." The same immunizing measure might also be recommended for some of those office Christmas parties.

By now I seem to hear a clamor from some belligerent readers who challenge Dr. Greenberg's arithmetic as it applies to themselves. They insist they can take more drinks than he specifies without feeling high. Let us see.

The highballs and Old-Fashioned cocktails drunk by Mr. Average contained exactly 1½ fluid ounces (a jigger) of 90-proof whiskey each, the dose you usually get in the more generous hotel bars. If the drinks you mix at home contain just one ounce (a pony) each, and if perchance your liquor was only 80 proof, some ciphering with a sharp pencil will convince you that the doctor was still right about drinks of full standard strength. Or perhaps you visit a bar whose extra-thick measuring glass looks generous enough, but which actually dispenses only seven eighths of an ounce of spirit. Of course, the less alcohol in the drink, the more drinks you can hold.

But beware of home-mixed highballs served by those overly hospitable hosts who slug your glass with two ounces of liquor, with sometimes a dividend added; those are liquid dynamite.

And make special note that the cocktails that are being counted are Old-Fashioneds—which contain nothing but whiskey, sugar, a dash of bitters, ice, and a squirt of seltzer—not Manhattans, which contain vermouth in addition to the whiskey. In a standard two-to-one Manhattan, made with 1½ ounces of whiskey plus ¾ ounce of 20 per cent vermouth, you get more than one fifth more absolute alcohol than in an Old-Fashioned. Four such Manhattans are almost equivalent to five Old-Fashioneds.

More challenges will be heard from beer and wine drinkers, who know that their beverages are less intoxicating than distilled spirits. Dr. Greenberg's classic doses provide for this, too. His single highball and Old-Fashioned each contain .675 fluid ounce of absolute alcohol; his 3½ ounce glass of sherry, which is 20 per cent alcohol by volume, contains .7 ounce; his 6 ounces of 12 per cent table wine represent .72 ounce; and his two bottles of 4½ per cent beer contain 1.08 fluid ounces of alcohol. In other words, wine and beer, because they contain food substances that slow absorption, release their alcohol into the blood more slowly than distilled spirits do; and Mr. Average has to drink larger quantities of these two beverages to get the same peak alcoholic effect.

Hold on again! says the beer drinker. Can anybody down ten bottles of beer—within a half-pint of a whole gallon—at a single sitting? While it has been done, thereby accounting for the fabulously enlarged stomachs of some legendary tosspots, the feat is impossible for an average human. Hence the brewing industry's claim that it is impossible to get drunk on beer.

But when is one drunk? The Russians, whose standard serving of straight 80-proof vodka is 3½ ounces—more than twice the amount of alcohol in an American drink—have a proverb: "When thy neighbor's face begins to flush, leave off drinking." An American expression is that "when the hands of your watch begin to wave at you, you have had enough."

The legal definition of intoxication, recognized in the courts of most states, is a blood-alcohol level of .15 per cent—the effect of five of these drinks before dinner. But seven world medical authorities who conferred at the University of Indiana in 1958 said this: "It is the opinion of this committee that a blood-alcohol concentration of .05 per cent will definitely impair the driving ability of some individuals . . . and at a concentration of .10 per cent all individuals are definitely impaired." And in Norway you would be thrown into jail if you were caught driving with more than .05 per cent alcohol in your blood (which is less than the effect of two drinks), even if there had been no accident.

Despite these sobering facts, few drinking drivers have ever been convicted in American courts when their blood tests showed less than .15 per cent alcohol. Since millions of Americans every day drive home after a round of drinks, despite all of the "If-You-Drink-Don't-Drive" sloganeering, common sense might indicate that it is time for a different approach to the problem of drunken driving.

How long you must wait after how many drinks, of what kinds, might be a better guide. To be specific, if you have had two beers, you had better wait an hour before driving, or three hours if you have had two highballs. If you are in a hurry to get home, it is better to move over in silent dignity and let your wife take the wheel. If she isn't sober either, a taxicab is at least more comfortable than an ambulance.

Let us now consider the much mutated Martini. This brings to mind the story of the Chicagoan who walked up to a bar and ordered ten Martinis all to be served to him at once. When they were placed in front of him he walked to the street and emptied two of the drinks on the sidewalk. Asked why, he replied: "The first one always makes me dizzy and the last one always makes me drunk." There may be no point to this tale, except that the average single Martini served in American bars hits harder than Dr. Greenberg's Old-Fashioned cocktails do; it does make the average drinker dizzy.

Since World War II the Martini has virtually ceased to be a cocktail. It has become, instead, a hooker of gin. No longer diluted with enough vermouth to weaken its power, some ten-to-one Martinis deliver nearly two ounces of 90-proof gin, thinned only by stirring with ice—almost nine tenths of an ounce of absolute alcohol.

There is still another reason why Martinis are so deadly: gin packs more wallop than whiskey of equal strength, because gin gets into your blood faster and produces a higher blood-alcohol peak. (You also burn it up faster than you do whiskey, if that is of any help.) A single "extra-dry" Martini can alcoholize your blood to .054 per cent, more than enough to get you arrested in Norway. The same amount of whiskey taken neat will just barely do that.

To this the defenders of gin reply that their beverage, by making itself felt quickly, warns you to slow down; whereas the whiskey customer, feeling little sensation at first, may gulp another drink while he is waiting. Eventually both whiskeys creep up and lay him low.

Is there any difference between long drinks (highballs, Collinses, fizzes) and cocktails like Martinis, Manhattans, and Old-Fashioneds in the amount of total alcohol you can hold? Yes, in general you will get less alcoholic effect from a long one that is made with the same total dose of liquor. This is not only because you drink the greater volume of liquid more slowly, but because dilution slows the rate of absorption into the blood. Moreover, a person who gets tipsy on whiskey highballs will sober up enough to drive home appreciably earlier than another who has taken the same amount of liquor in straight shots.

I am often asked to rate the various popular drinks according to their relative potency at the time they are drunk. In terms of comparative alcohol concentrations, this is simple enough. It has been computed carefully, taking into consideration the degrees to which cocktails and highballs become diluted by the water from melting ice. But the variations are wide because of the differences in strengths and quantities of liquor dispensed by different bartenders. However, to answer the question: the highest concentration is in a straight shot of 100-proof bottled-in-bond whiskey or brandy, which is 50 per cent alcohol; next come the gins, whiskeys, rums, brandies, and vodkas that range from 80 to 90 proof (40 to 45 per cent); the cordials, from 25 up to 55 per cent; Martinis, 34 to 40 per cent; Manhattans, 30 to 36; Old-Fashioneds, 25 to 30; highballs, 9 to 20; dessert wines and vermouths, 16 to 20; table and sparkling wines, 9 to 14; ale, 5 to 7.5; and, finally, beer, roughly 4 to 6 per cent.

The foregoing at least suggests the advisability of carefully noting on bottle labels the proof of your spirituous liquors and the alcoholic strength of your wines. A drink of 100-proof whiskey, for example, contains one fourth more alcohol than the same quantity of whiskey at 80 proof. Port wine contains two thirds more than burgundy. And as a later chapter tells you, ale and malt liquor are stronger than beer.

But do not swallow all of the stories you hear about the terrific jolt somebody once got from this liquor or that. Especially, don't believe it about Grandma's homemade elderberry wine, which—unless Grandma spiked it with brandy—wasn't over 11 per cent. The earthquake effects attributed to such drinks are mostly in the imbiber's upper story.

Now we come to the hollow-leg folks—the ones who insist they can take a dozen cocktails before they feel the faintest buzz. They are firmly convinced that because they are experienced drinkers, they have developed a tolerance for alcohol—that their bodies have learned to burn it up faster. The truth is not what they think. Some people do learn to navigate and behave themselves under the handicap of a little liquor, but their tolerance is purely psychological, not physiological. They are like the tightrope walker who has learned to balance himself without solid support.

Intensive research into metabolism rates has failed to show that anybody can materially speed the rate at which his liver oxidizes alcohol. Besides, those who complain of a hollow leg have usually been drinking after a heavy meal. If they are seeking intoxication after filling their stomachs with food, they are using a great deal of expensive liquor to little avail. Today's custom of before-dinner drinking may well have evolved from this, as a measure of economy.

At the other extreme there is the person who becomes deathly ill after a single cocktail. Chances are that he merely swallows his liquor too quickly. His stomach, unaccustomed to the shock, reacts; his pyloric valve clamps shut, and nausea follows. However, there are some people whose systems always react this way, even if they drink slowly. They are fortunate in that at least they are immune to excessive drinking.

There also are times when one drink before dinner hits the individual harder than two drinks did on an earlier similar occasion. This can result from fatigue or hunger—conditions in which the blood-sugar level is low, and in which the effect of alcohol is thereby magnified.

As for the ways a drinker's moods can cause the influence of alcohol upon him to vary, many things have been observed, but diligent researchers have thus far been able to find very few patterns of behavior that apply to all individuals. Well-adjusted people readily become merry after a minimum number of drinks, but those whose behavior is normally phlegmatic seem to tolerate more liquor than their companions do before they show it. Whatever one's mood, a little alcohol usually exaggerates the way he expresses it, because this drug anesthetizes his self-critical judgment. Those who feel happy or frisky act tipsy sooner, and those who are angry or suspicious often become angrier or more suspicious when they drink. O. Henry wrote of vivacious, excitable people that some men are "half drunk when they are sober." He well might have added that a few drinks can make them a thorough nuisance.

Is it true that a person shows his true nature when he is drunk, as when a normally meek individual becomes loud and abusive after several drinks? My psychiatrist friends say no. Instead, they explain, such aggressive behavior represents long-pent-up resentments and emotional pressures that the person has suppressed while sober but which are released when alcohol deadens his inhibitions.

The important effects emotions exert on our physical condition and behavior can be illustrated by the remarkable cures doctors accomplish by prescribing placebos—sugar pills—for many of their patients' ills. The varying moods and blood-sugar levels of tense individuals may make them require more alcohol for relaxation at some times than at others.

But regardless of all such differences, it is important to remember that anyone who lets his blood-alcohol level reach .15 per cent is thoroughly drunk, regardless of how he felt when he began drinking.

Although it is assumed that you want to avoid intoxication, it is necessary also to tell you what happens when people take many times the amount of liquor they can hold. It can be told rather simply. Anyone who raises the alcohol content of his blood to .4 of one per cent—which can happen to an average man if he quickly drinks a pint and a half of hard liquor—passes out cold. If he manages to gulp enough, before losing consciousness, to reach .7 of one per cent—as a man in Dayton, Ohio, did by drinking sixteen Martinis to win a bet—his breathing is paralyzed, and he is dead.

Having now disposed of the foregoing gruesome statistic, it seems advisable to condense, for practical use by the reader,

DRINKOMETER

Effects of Drinks According to Body Weight

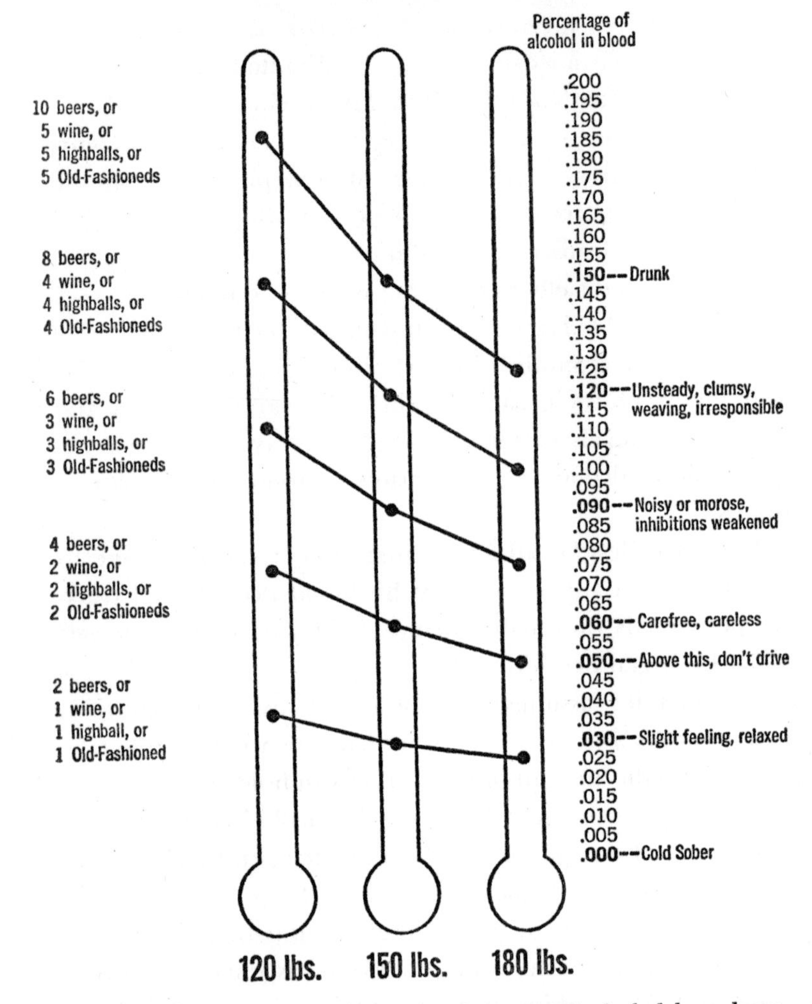

Based on 12-oz. bottles of beer containing 4½% alcohol by volume, 6-oz. servings of 12% wine, 3½-oz. servings of 20% wine, and highballs or Old-Fashioned cocktails containing one jigger (1½ oz.) of 90-proof whiskey, taken on an empty stomach within a short time.

Estimated Percentage of Alcohol in Blood by Number of Drinks in Relation to Body Weight*

Highballs or cocktails or equivalent in wine or beer		1	2	3	4	5	6	7	8
BODY WEIGHT	100 lb.	.045	.090	.135	.180	.225	.270	.315	.360
	120 lb.	.037	.075	.112	.150	.187	.224	.262	.300
	140 lb.	.032	.064	.096	.129	.160	.192	.225	.258
	160 lb.	.028	.056	.084	.112	.140	.168	.197	.224
	180 lb.	.025	.050	.075	.100	.125	.150	.175	.200
	200 lb.	.022	.045	.068	.090	.112	.136	.155	.180

Based on highballs or cocktails containing 1½ oz. (one jigger) of 90-proof spirits taken on an empty stomach within a short time. Each such drink is equivalent to one 3½-oz. serving of 20% appetizer or dessert wine, or to one 6-oz. serving of 12 % table wine, or to 2 bottles of beer containing 4½% alcohol by volume.

Safety Zone

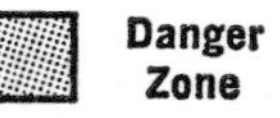
Danger Zone

Unconscious

* Adapted from a chart prepared by the New Jersey Department of Law and Public Safety.

the most important kinds of guidance that have been offered in this chapter. On page 28 is what I call my Drinkometer, which gives you in an eyeful the number of drinks of certain kinds that produce various levels of alcohol in the blood, in relation to the drinker's body weight. The Drinkometer gives this for persons weighing 120-, 150-, and 180-pounds. For those weighing more or less than these amounts, similar information is given in the table on page 29. To use these figures, remember that they are based on Dr. Greenberg's measured doses of 90-proof whiskey, in highballs and Old-Fashioned (not Manhattan) cocktails, of 20 per cent dessert wine, of 12 per cent table wine, and of 4½ per cent beer, taken on an empty stomach within a short time; and that some people feel their drinks more than others.

Sobering-up Time

How soon can you drive after drinking? The New Jersey Department of Law and Public Safety distributes cards to bar patrons containing a blood-alcohol chart and an approximate method of computing sobering-up times after a given number of drinks taken over various periods of hours.

Since vision and judgment are affected in varying degrees when the concentration of alcohol in your blood exceeds even .030 per cent, it is dangerous to drive a car until your body has at least had time to burn up enough of your drinks to reach that level. The National Safety Council has shown that the .030 level impairs driving ability. At more than .050 per cent the driver is a public menace.

To compute your sobering-up time, first count the number of drinks you have taken. Second, determine the per cent of alcohol that could be produced in your blood from all of those drinks in relation to your body weight, using the Drinkometer or the table on the facing page. Third, subtract from this figure the per cent of blood alcohol burned up during the time that has elapsed since your first drink. This is done by subtracting .015 per cent for each hour. The remainder is an estimate of the per cent of alcohol remaining in your blood. Thus, in one hour, if your liver is normal, your blood-alcohol level drops .015 per cent; in two hours it drops .030 per cent; in three hours .045 per cent; in four hours .060 per cent; in five hours .075 per cent; in six hours .090 per cent.

For example, if you weigh 150 pounds and have had four highballs of 90-proof whiskey over a period of six hours, your blood-alcohol level is down to .030 per cent (.120 per cent minus .090 per cent).

CHAPTER 5

Spirits Are Strongest

IF YOU ARE HOPELESSLY CONFUSED ABOUT WHISKEYS, GINS, brandies, rums, vodkas, bonds, straights, blends, and such, don't ask your liquor dealer to enlighten you. He can tell you a great deal about these subjects, but most of what he knows isn't true. Bombarded with distillers' claims for the products they sell him, aware of the snob appeal of expensive brands, concerned with his store's bottle profit margins, he is usually worse confused than you are.

You also will learn little from the splendorous liquor advertisements that praise a spirit's "lightness," "smoothness," "subtle richness," or its "full-bodied downright goodness" without giving you the faintest clue to how the glamorized firewater actually tastes or how it would affect you if you were to buy and drink it.

Are expensive liquors better? Is sour-mash whiskey sweet? Does age really matter? Is vodka just alcohol? How about gins, rums, tequila, aquavit, slivovitz? Why does rye "burn" going down?

To answer such questions frankly and to unscramble briefly each of the principal spirituous liquors that you find in American stores—perhaps risking some distillers' wrath by explaining their products too simply—is the naïve purpose of this and the two following chapters.

All these distilled spirits are potent, usually ten times as strong as beer, three or four times as strong as table wines.

You should know what makes them so: If you boiled a pot of freshly fermented beer, and captured and condensed the escaping vapor, the resulting liquid would somewhat resemble a raw new whiskey. If you boiled wine, and condensed the vapor, you would have a new (unaged) brandy. Distilling is that simple: alcohol boils and vaporizes at 172.5 degrees, leaving behind water, which boils at 212 degrees. (Don't try it at home, however; you would be distilling liquor illegally, which is a federal offense.) Distilling, as a way of concentrating the alcohol from such fermented drinks as beer and wine, has been going on in the Western world since the Middle Ages, although the Chinese knew how at least as early as 800 B.C.

Is this freshly condensed vapor (called spirit because it is the breath of life in all such beverages) the same liquor you get when you buy a bottle? No, not usually. For one thing, most spirits (not all!) are aged for varying periods of years, and their characters are changed thereby. For another, all new spirits are white, simply colorless; their color is acquired either from the barrel or from the addition of caramel. Some newly distilled liquors are twice as strong as what is normally sold. Most of those you get have been liberally diluted with distilled water to drinkable strength before bottling.

You should know the strength of what you buy. In the United States each bottle bears a statement of "proof," which means double the alcoholic content by volume; 100 proof means 50 per cent alcohol, 80 proof means 40 per cent, and so on. Liquor strengths in this country have been declining, although the public seems scarcely to have noticed the change (perhaps because the proof is often hidden on the back label). If you are in Canada, you are completely befuddled about "proof," which means something else in that country and is seldom stated on liquor bottles there.

Are There Bargains in Liquor?

In nothing else that you buy do you pay so much for so little original value as in your purchase of spirituous liquor. This is because, in a typical $4.43 "fifth" bottle of spirits, federal and state excise taxes represent 55 per cent of the retail price, or $2.42. That leaves $2.01 for the liquor, the bottle, the labor, shipping costs, and the "overhead" and profits of the maker, the wholesaler, and storekeeper.

(These figures are national averages for 86.8-proof whiskey. The federal government takes $1.89, state and local taxes average 53 cents per bottle. The state tax bite varies; in Arkansas you would pay 27 cents more, in North Dakota 47 cents more, for the same bottle of liquor.)

When you consider that this same quantity of new whiskey —fresh from the still, before it goes into a barrel—can be made for anywhere from ten cents to a quarter, you get an idea of why moonshining continues to be a billion-dollar-a-year business in the United States. Yet moonshine is no bargain, as we shall see in a moment.

Are there any bargains in spirits? Yes, but you have to experiment to find them. An unadvertised brand, usually named for the store that sells it, may taste fully as good as another brand that is nationally famous. But again, a cheap whiskey may taste grainy because it is young, harsh, and bitter from excessive aging, or unpleasant for other reasons; you have no way of knowing before you buy it.

Furthermore, when you get a cheap bottle that is good, the next bottle may be entirely different. So if you find a low-priced liquor you happen to like, hurry back to the same store and get more bottles from the same case, gambling that the rest will be identical.

This situation exists especially in whiskey, because most distilleries have many batches in their warehouses. They use the best for their own brands, and sell in bulk to one another, or to the nation's several dozen liquor brokers, any odd lots for which they have no use. The brokers peddle to rectifier bottlers, and the latter bottle the so-called private brands, the poorest of which are called "cheapies." Some high-grade retailers have enough liquor knowledge and buying power to insist on getting consistent, good-quality liquors under their house labels. But your only way to be sure of what you are getting is to stick with the nationally advertised brands, whose owners have too much at stake to risk selling you poor quality.

If the label says "distilled and bottled by" a leading distiller, you at least know the liquor was bottled where it was made. But many of the best liquor labels do not say this, because the distiller may have had the bottling done elsewhere. The brand means much more than the bottling legend.

Is it true that a single distiller sells the same whiskey under different labels? Yes, this is often done, but the leading companies see to it that when the liquor is the same, the prices of such brands are also identical.

There is little use in shopping from store to store for bargains in a single brand, because most states with privately licensed stores maintain rigid enforcement of brand price posting, while in a "monopoly" state, where the state owns and operates all the stores, there obviously can be no price cutting.

In liquor buying, the main things to watch are the proof on the label (which signifies how much spirit and how much diluting water you are getting) and the size of the bottle. An 80-proof liquor, on which less federal tax has been paid, sells for less than 86 proof or 100. And of course the large economy-size bottles usually (but not always) give you more for your money than small ones do. A quart (32 ounces) is also a better bargain than a "fifth" (25.6 ounces), and a pint (16 ounces) gives you more liquor than a "tenth" (12.8 ounces) does. Inside Canada, too, there are size differences; Canadian liquors are sold there in 25-ounce bottles, while the imported kinds come in containers with two thirds of an ounce more.

How Moonshiners Cheat

Those who buy bootleg liquor not only run the risk of being poisoned, but also help to keep our taxes high and to support organized crime. Moonshining is not merely the southern hillbilly's side line amusingly pictured in a comic strip, where he plays hide-and-seek with the "revenooers." Illegal liquor is everwhere—in New York, Pennsylvania, New Jersey, Maryland, Delaware, Michigan, Illinois, and all other states, cheating the government, which means all taxpayers, out of $750,000,000 in taxes each year.

Beware of bottles that are represented as "stolen" or as "smuggled"; of those surreptitiously sold in after-hours "breakfast clubs," and of the ones poured in the frowsier bars. The brand labels may look genuine, but make sure the strip stamp over the bottle's mouth has not been tampered with. The law requires immediate destruction of every spirits bottle that is emptied, but too many are saved to reappear, refilled with moonshine. When you empty a bottle, put a knife through the label, then smash the bottle inside a double paper bag.

This is for your own protection, because wherever you live it is more than likely that there is moonshine in your neighborhood. Almost one fourth of all the spirits now drunk in the United States is illegal, counterfeit merchandise!

Some of it is highly dangerous, concocted from paint solvent and antifreeze that may contain deadly wood (methyl) alcohol, which blinds its victims before it kills them. The rest is cleverly doctored to taste like genuine liquor.

The secrets your friendly bootleggers learned during fifteen years of national prohibition have been handed down to their repeal era successors. Prune juice, raisins, glycerin, charred wood chips, and other flavorings, plus beading oil and caramel coloring, transform alcohol into imitation aged whiskey. Creosote helps imitate the smoky flavor of Scotch, with added iodine to "burn going down." Essences of bourbon, rum, and cognac are still supplied wholesale to city moonshiners. And druggists everywhere still sell oil of juniper and compound spirits of orange, which, with glycerin and alcohol made the better bathtub gin of prohibition days.

So enormous has been the moonshine industry's growth in certain southern states that in 1955 it led to a unique social experiment. Officials of the North Carolina Alcohol Control Board were deeply concerned. In 1953 no less than 3,627 illegal stills had been seized in their state. But the flow of illegal liquor, instead of being interrupted, grew; still seizures rose to 3,846 in the following year. It seemed the hillbillies preferred homemade white lightning—raw, unaged, colorless "corn squeezin's"—to the yellowish corn whiskey legally sold throughout the South.

Something obviously had to be done. State and county officials consulted a large distiller, and the "something" was agreed upon: the state must fight white lightning with stronger white lightning. The Lynndale Distillery Company made a batch of corn whiskey at 100 proof, bottled it with less than thirty days' age, and it went on sale to compete with the 70- to 75-proof moonshine. The label read: "White Lightning Corn Whiskey—'Clear as the Mountain Dew.' "

The entire lot was quickly sold out. More White Lightning was made, sales spread to a dozen other states, and more distilling companies joined the campaign. At the present writing this legal moonshine is still sold throughout most of North Carolina.

Strange Story of "Proof"

As strange as is our custom of stating liquor strength in degrees of "proof" is the story of how the custom began. Equally strange is that its origin was forgotten for almost half a century, and was finally unearthed after 1900. An old English dictionary supplied the explanation: "proof" meant "gunpowder proof."

It seems that in an earlier, more primitive era, distillers had no way of determining a spirit's strength until someone hit on the idea of burning it with gunpowder. A flame was touched to a mixture of liquor and powder. If the mix failed to ignite, the spirit was too weak. If it flared up too brightly, it was too strong. But if it burned steadily with a bright blue flame, this was "proof" that the spirit was right.

When less crude methods finally determined that "proof spirit" was approximately 57 per cent alcohol by volume, the British Government in 1816 adopted that figure as official. Later America copied the idea, but amended the figure, defining 50 per cent alcohol as "100 proof." This made it easy to translate alcohol strength to proof by simply doubling the per cent by volume.

But the British have never changed. Today in Britain and Canada "proof" still means 57.1 per cent alcohol by volume, 114.2 proof American. America's 100 proof is "12.5 U. P." (Under Proof). By the confusing British Sykes scale, the smaller the "U. P." figure, the greater the liquor's strength. Absolute alcohol (200-proof American), a product used only in laboratories, is "75.25 O. P." (Over Proof) British Sykes.

Luckily for Canadian consumers, Dominion spirits sold at home are not labeled with their strength. By government stipulation during World War II all Canadian liquor was reduced from "24.7 U. P." (86-proof American) to "30 U. P." (80 American), the standard effective in Britain since World War I.

It is unfortunate from the moderation standpoint that "proof" ever appeared on American labels. Why? Because "100 per cent" is a cultural shibboleth in this country. It somehow conveys to Americans the meaning of "genuine"; anything less seems unacceptable. And 100-proof liquor is much too strong to drink straight.

CHAPTER 6

Whiskeys Unscrambled

NOW, SUPPOSE YOU WOULD LIKE TO BUY A BOTTLE OF GOOD whiskey. The assortment of types and prices on store shelves and back bars is bewildering. What is a "good" whiskey, anyhow? If you happen to know someone who is called "a gentleman, a scholar, and a judge of good whiskey," and are so inconsiderate as to ask him that question, he either will be stumped or will be wrong, because he doesn't know. I have asked it of at least a hundred professional experts and have gotten a hundred different replies. Put all their answers together, however, discard what makes no sense, and the facts add up to this:

There was a time when fermenting and distilling were crudely done, and some whiskeys consequently had foul, unclean, disagreeable flavors and odors. In pre-prohibition times, too, bars and liquor stores bought new, raw whiskey by the barrel, doctoring it with flavoring, coloring, smoothing materials, and "beading oil" (the latter to make their liquor stick to the glass). Such whiskeys were bad; the rest were regarded as good.

Few actually foul whiskeys are made nowadays, except by moonshiners, but some legal whiskeys are excessively harsh, or lack character, or are bitter and woody tasting from excessive or improper aging.

The highest quality test any whiskey can meet is that it has a flavor you happen to like, that the same flavor lasts each time you sip it, that it is smooth, not harsh, and that it leaves a pleasant aftertaste—what the distillers call "a good farewell."

The foregoing definition of "good" applies regardless of the whiskey's type, age, or origin. It can stand, also, for other liquors—brandy, rum, gin, arrack, tequila, slivovitz, okolehao—in fact, for most distillates except vodka. We shall get to all of them presently.

Most of what you read about the types of whiskey tells you in scrupulous detail how they are made—about which you probably care little or not at all—not how they taste, which is what you might like to know. For example, the United States Government meticulously defines, in its maze of regulations that govern all liquor sold, no less than thirty-one whiskey types (thirteen of which do not even exist!) in detailed manufacturing terms, and without an enlightening word about their flavors. All whiskeys are distillates of fermented mashes of grain; bourbon is mostly corn with some rye and barley; rye whiskey uses more rye than corn; Scotch is barley and corn.

I once reduced the thousands of kinds of wine to just thirty-three flavors. Having not yet been challenged for such audacity, I now declare that there are only seven flavors of whiskey. They are bourbon, rye, corn, spirit blend, Canadian, Scotch, and Irish. Here is how they differ in taste.

Bourbon is rich, faintly sweetish, faintly vanilla-like, and you can taste in it the new charred-oak barrel from which this whiskey gets most of its flavor. (The Bourbon Institute, which has spent thousands of dollars in its search for words to describe bourbon's flavor, is unlikely to approve of mine.)

Rye tastes of the new charred barrel, too, but its strong rye-like flavor from rye grain makes it differ from bourbon the way in which rye bread differs from white. Rye is usually heavier in flavor substances than bourbon.

Corn whiskey has a sharp alcoholic taste, because it is sold with little aging, and a slight grainy flavor of corn. It has virtually no wood taste because the barrels it is stored in are usually not new. Its color is yellowish, almost white, while other whiskeys are pale to reddish or dark amber.

Spirit blends (the labels say "blended whiskey" or "whiskey—a blend") usually have a bourbon taste, but their flavor is softened and lightened because from three fifths to four fifths of the liquor they contain is new neutral spirits—a euphemism for almost-pure alcohol.

Canadian whiskeys taste pretty much like spirit blends, because that is what they are, except that the proportion of neutral spirits (alcohol) they contain is considerably less, and the Canadian neutral spirits are aged, not new. Canadian whiskey has a little more rye flavor than United States blended whiskeys, and little or no charred-barrel flavor because the Canadians seldom use new barrels.

Scotch whisky (the Scots spell it without the "e") has a burnt-malt, pungent, smoky taste, from the peat-fire-dried barley malt in its mash. It reminds some people of iodine, others of shoe leather. Scotch is a spirit blend, also, diluted with alcohol to a greater extent than Canadian. It is stored in reused barrels and lacks any charred-oak flavor.

Irish whiskey is somewhat like Scotch, but without the smoke. Both have a character that results from the old-style pot stills they use, but the Irish has more malty flavor. And perhaps because exported Scotches have tended since mid-century to have much less flavor than formerly, some of the Irish distillers have done the reverse, shipping their flavorful Old Country whiskeys to America.

The foregoing, I assert, are the seven flavors of whiskeys. And now, because my descriptions will surely be disputed, I must defend them.

The first and loudest protest should come from the rye drinkers of the Atlantic seaboard and Canada. The "rye" they drink doesn't taste at all like my description. To them I say: "You only *think* you are drinking rye. Look at the bottle and you will see. The label reads 'blended whiskey'; it does not even mention rye."

"But I *order* rye," says the New Yorker. Yes, you do, but you are served a spirit blend. Ten to one you have never tasted real rye. In fact, if you have ever visited the West Coast (where this particular kind of confusion does not exist), and have ordered a drink of rye there, you probably did not like it, because genuine rye is what you got!

This strange, rather amusing name garbling exists because in the minds of most Easterners and Canadians there are only two kinds of whiskey—Scotch and "rye." Such other whiskeys as bourbon, spirit blends, and Canadian, because they are not Scotch, are assumed to be rye. The origin of the tangle goes back many years. Before prohibition the principal whiskey sold in most states east of Kentucky was real, straight rye from the distilleries of Pennsylvania and Maryland. During prohibition the medicinal whiskey your father got on his doctor's prescription was also this same pre-prohibition rye. When, during those "dry" years, vast quantities of Scotch and Canadian whiskeys were smuggled into this country, the Canadian whiskey was also assumed to be rye, simply because the label did not say it wasn't. As a result, to this day, when you say "rye" to the average New York bartender, you are merely telling him you don't want Scotch. He may even sometimes serve you a bourbon.

You can get real rye, of course, by insisting on a bottle that is so labeled. Rye connoisseurs know this, and order rye by their favorite brand names. But straight ryes have faded from popularity. By 1959 the only places where they still enjoyed much favor were the two states where most ryes are still made—Maryland and Pennsylvania.

Confusion about whiskey types is not confined to the East and Canada. In the West, too, people think of only two kinds of whiskey—Scotch and bourbon. When you order bourbon in California, the bartender often pours from a bottled labeled "blended whiskey."

I have long been told that rye "burns more going down." But being skeptical of all such legends, I decided one evening to perform an experiment. With the help of my liquor merchant neighbor, Juan Hayes, I assembled a dozen kinds of distilled spirits and a half-dozen willing human guinea pigs, and held a "blind" liquor tasting.

First, I carefully diluted the higher-proof samples with water, in order that all would be the same 86-proof strength. Then each participant, unaware of which sample he was tasting, was instructed to record on a written ballot the degree of "burning sensation" he felt from each. This was faithfully done.

When the scores were totted up (the following morning!) rye led all the rest. Straight bourbons took the next three places; Scotch was third, blends were far down the list.

I do not claim that our experiment was conclusive, but if the outcome happened to be right, a possible reason has already been stated: ryes—at least those sold in my neighborhood—are markedly heavier in flavor substances than most other whiskies. It is generally believed, although scientific verification still is lacking, that the more pronounced flavor an alcoholic drink has, the more it is felt as it passes down the drinker's gullet.

Now to face the indignant Canadians and Scots, who will furiously deny my earlier statement that their whiskeys are diluted with neutral spirits (plain, flavorless alcohol) and are therefore actually spirit blends. This hotly disputed subject needs clearing up, in the next several paragraphs, for those readers who are spirit cognoscenti.

First, remember that the more a spirit is concentrated (the higher the proof at which it is distilled), the more nearly pure it is—and the less flavor it has. Real (straight) whiskey is usually distilled at well below 140 proof, and therefore has a great deal of flavor. Neutral spirits are distilled at 190 proof, contain scarcely any flavor substances, and therefore have no flavor.

Look at the labels and advertising of American "blended whiskeys" and you see statements like this, which are required by the United States Government: "35 per cent straight whiskey, 65 per cent grain neutral spirits." Some labels say as little as 20 per cent straight whiskey, some 30, some as high as 40, but all say "neutral spirits."

Labels of Canadian and Scotch never mention either neutral spirits or straight whiskey. All they say is that they are "blended."

The facts are these: Both Canadian and Scotch whiskeys *do* contain high-proof, neutral, flavorless alcohol, but those countries do not call it neutral spirits. By a semantical dodge they call it "grain whiskey." They claim it is not really neutral because it is distilled at slightly lower proof than American neutral spirits (at 180 to 188 proof instead of 190). Furthermore, they age their "grain whiskey" together with their flavorful straight whiskey, whereas United States distillers age their straight whiskey but usually add the neutral spirits while the latter is new.

In an average bottle of Scotch, about three-fourths of the contents are this neutral "grain whiskey." The Canadian product does not need quite that much, because Canadian straight whiskeys—before the "grain whiskey" is added—are already more neutral (distilled at much higher proofs) than most United States whiskeys are.

Why don't American distillers make their blends with "grain whiskey" the way the Canadians, the Scots, and some of the Irish do? Because our federal regulations do not allow it for whiskeys made in this country. As a result United States blended whiskeys, some of which cost more to produce than certain straights do, are cheapened in the public mind by the compulsory reference in their labels and advertisements to "neutral spirits," while the imports are exempt from this requirement.

This is only one strange highlight of the incredibly weird liquor picture in the United States. The whole whiskey-making industry is wrapped in a lopsided strait jacket of outworn laws and regulations and centuries-old traditions, tightened by the pressures of internal and international politics, that prevent it from progressing as other industries have. Old-line Kentucky distillers block any changes that might benefit spirit blends, while foreign producers and importers lobby to preserve the special privileges their whiskeys enjoy in this country.

A classic example of the latter is the peculiar regulation that forbids an age statement on United States bourbon or rye whiskey that has been stored in a secondhand barrel, while imported whiskeys, which are regularly aged in reused barrels, freely proclaim their age on labels and in advertising.

Equally strange are the artificial barriers that prevent United States distillers from making American Scotch whiskey. Credit these to British diplomacy, aided and abetted by our State Department. The making of Scotch, despite all the myths about Scottish geography and climate, requires only the crudest equipment, plus grains, peat, and water that are obtainable anywhere. One Illinois distiller actually brought an entire distillery from Scotland, even including a supply of Scotch peat, to make some. Experts could not distinguish it from the imported. But the words "Scotch type," which our government compelled the firm to print on its labels, effectively smothered its sale; and now even a "Scotch-type" American whiskey is prohibited. And the largest United States liquor companies have lately resorted to buying their own distilleries in Scotland.

Canada had a similar experience. The Canadian distillers, despite angry protests from Scotland, eventually won a partial victory. Their Dominion government now allows them to make Canadian Scotch, but they may only label it "Highland Whisky."

Many American whiskey producers wish they could retire their traditions and make full use of modern technology. They see beer- and wine-making science progressing steadily, but there are no whiskey distilling schools in this country. For one hundred and seventy years distillers have been burning the insides of new oak barrels, which now cost twenty-five dollars each, simply because liquor was originally flavored that way one hundred and seventy years ago. They are actually proud of this primitive method. One company held a million-dollar public contest seeking ideas on how to use the two million barrels bourbon makers discard annually after storing whiskey in them only once. Experts have admitted to me privately that they could easily make better-tasting whiskey without the years of costly aging now required, if only their old-fashioned ways were not frozen by traditions, laws, and regulations. They could even make "instant whiskey"!

Have you ever wondered how the various whiskeys came to taste as they do? If some of their flavors please you while others make you gag, their origins may be of some interest.

The Irish invented whiskey. Tradition says St. Patrick, who lived in the fifth century, taught them how. They called it *uisge beatha* (water of life). The English invaders found the drink palatable, but the name was too much to swallow, so they renamed it "whiskey." The original Irish liquor was heavily flavored with saffron, licorice, nutmeg, and other spices, but it gradually evolved to blends of straight pot-still whiskeys, with some "grain whiskey" blends.

Scotland apparently learned the distilling art from Ireland. The early Scotches were straight whiskeys, until in Charles Dickens' time distillers learned to dilute them with tasteless "grain whiskeys." This made Scotch palatable to the then brandy-drinking English.

In colonial America the first popular spirit was rum, which the Puritans mixed with hard cider to make a drink called, fittingly, "Stone Wall." The first whiskey made in the eastern colonies was strong-tasting rye. George Washington grew rye at Mount Vernon and is said to have had a still near there. As farmers migrated westward, they discovered that the cheapest way to transport their grain to the seacoast was to distill it into whiskey. A horse that could carry only four bushels of grain could easily transport the whiskey made from twenty-four bushels. It kept longer, and was used in place of money when the Continental currency lost its value.

Then came the Whiskey Rebellion, "Washington's second

war," which influenced both the course of American history and the taste of its liquor. In 1791 an excise tax of nine cents a gallon was leveled on whiskey. Pennsylvania farmers, virtually all of whom had stills, refused to pay the tax, and the President in 1794 sent a force of militia to enforce it. This bloodless coup, which established the young nation's taxing power, also sent many disgruntled farmer-distillers farther west, away from the tax collectors. In Kentucky, where corn is the principal grain, bourbon was born.

Corn, distilled by itself, makes an insipid-tasting liquor. Some Kentucky distillers added rye to their mashes, but the main credit for creating the flavor of today's bourbon whiskey is generally given to a Baptist minister of Georgetown, in what was then Bourbon County, Kentucky. In 1789 the Reverend Elijah Craig, according to currently accepted lore, introduced the charred-oak barrel, which gives bourbon, a liquor made mainly from corn, its principal taste.

Whether the Reverend Craig was really the first to age whiskey in charred barrels is debatable, but he was the first to whom it brought undying fame. There are several legends to explain its beginning, among which the following is regarded as the most plausible. The early Midwestern distillers, lacking new barrels in which to store their liquor, turned to the empty kegs that had brought salted fish from New England. Experimenting, they found that by burning the inside of each stave they could rid the wood of its fishy smell and taste. At first the liquor's strange reddish color, obtained from the char, caused drinkers to spurn it as poison, and only those who could not afford uncolored whiskey would buy it. Eventually connoisseurs discovered that the burnt wood smoothed and mellowed the liquor and gave it entirely new flavors.

The Kentucky distillers now claim that their bourbons

cannot be duplicated anywhere because the water in which they cook their grain comes from subterranean limestone deposits. Makers of bourbon in Illinois, Indiana, California, and other states have a simple answer to this. "We distill whiskey, not water," they say.

Labels that say "sour-mash straight whiskey" are another Kentucky specialty. Those consumers who insist that this is the only kind of whiskey they like might be surprised to learn that virtually all American whiskeys nowadays are made by the same "sour-mash" process, whether their labels say so or not. Incidentally, this manufacturing method (which involves adding some of yesterday's distilled mash to today's fermenting mash) tends to make a whiskey rich and sweet, not sour.

There is potent meaning, however, in another kind of straight-whiskey label that is not confined to Kentucky products. It says "bottled in bond," to which might be added "look out!" because this term means, in the United States, that the bottle's contents are fully 100 proof. There are people who refuse to buy any other whiskey, because they interpret the legend "bottled in bond under United States Government supervision" as a governmental guarantee of the liquor's quality. It is not. All it means is that the Internal Revenue Service has allowed the distiller to delay paying his tax until he was ready to sell this whiskey, a privilege the government allows only for 100-proof straight liquors that are at least four years old.

This is not the case in Canada, where the 80-proof Canadian whiskeys are all labeled "bottled in bond under supervision of the Canadian Government." When they come to this country the words "in bond" are expunged, but the rest of the legend is allowed to remain, allowing these imports still another advantage denied to most United States liquors.

There is wine in some whiskeys. In fact, virtually all spirit blends—which include Canadian and Scotch—contain a little wine, added as a smoothing agent. Some also use prune juice and St. John's bread (the sweetish pulp of the carob bean), but the principal softener of whiskey's rough edges is a special heavy-bodied sherry. Scotland goes other countries one better, not only adding sherry, but storing some Scotches in second-hand sherry casks (which the Irish do, too, with all their whiskeys) to give them winy flavor, polish, and color. But nothing can be added legally to United States straight whiskeys, not even the caramel (tasteless burnt sugar) that colors spirit blends. Straight whiskey must get its color solely from the barrel.

Have you noticed that whiskeys have changed lately, that many of them do not taste the way they formerly did? In the late 1950's there occurred a whiskey-flavor revolution. Suddenly the makers of many famous 100-proof "bonds" came out with 86-proof versions of their whiskeys. They even included some who had long sworn publicly that their old-style potent whiskeys would never change. Some whiskeys that had always been 90 proof dropped to 86, others leapfrogged down to 80. Successive batches of once-dark, brownish, heavily flavorful liquors turned increasingly pale and bland. Especially was this true of Scotches, which, although maintaining their 86-proof strength, grew less and less smoky in taste. Brands of "light" Scotch were advertised throughout the nation, and Scotch in general became a more bland spirit than formerly.

How far this trend may go in years to come remains to be seen, for whiskey drinkers' tastes are notoriously fickle. At any rate, the lowering of proofs at least is healthy, because the jigger that measures the liquor to go into your highball now delivers one fifth less alcohol wallop when filled from a bottle of 80-proof than from a bottle of 100-proof "bonded."

And if you think lowered proof alone does not change the taste of liquor, just remember the last time you visited Canada. Didn't the 80-proof whiskey you drank there taste smoother than the 86.8- and 90-proof versions of the same brands that Canada ships to this country?

Now, let us explode the myth of great age. As you probably already know, the number of years stated on a bottle represent only the time the liquor has spent in wooden barrels. This is because distilled spirits, unlike wines, do not improve after bottling. The bottle of "bonded" you have kept since before Pearl Harbor is still only four years old.

A visitor from England once commented that this country's liquor buyers suffer from "agephobia" because they pay the highest prices for whiskeys that claim the most years of age. The complex chemical changes that occur during spirits' aging—the gradual formation of esters and ethers, the creation of new flavor compounds by the interaction of alcohol and wood—are not fully understood, even by the leading distillers. What they do know is that different liquors mature at different times, and that too much age can be worse than not enough.

The newest whiskey will not make you any sicker, or cause you to cough any harder, than the most ancient spirit of the same kind. In so far as medical knowledge on this subject exists, the fact may even be the other way around. I have tasted water-white whiskey that was exactly one day old. Except for its fresh, rather grainy flavor, which aging would overcome, I did not find it at all unpleasant.

How old should whiskey be, then, to taste best? For bourbon and rye, stored in new charred-oak barrels, two years is regarded as minimum, four years as nearly ideal. Except for those of heaviest flavor, which can improve with an additional year or two, too much time in their barrels makes these kinds of whiskey taste excessively woody and harsh.

Canadian, Scotch, and Irish can stand more years in wood than bourbon or rye, but only because the countries making them use secondhand barrels. Scotch, which can be sold in Great Britain when it is three years old, must be at least four years old to enter the United States at a favorable duty rate. Twelve-year-old Scotch became scarce during World War II, when most Scotch labels dropped their age statements entirely.

The thing to keep in mind is that the taste is more important than what the label says. No amount of aging can make a bad whiskey good. Joe. E. Lewis once commented sagely on this moot subject. "Certainly whiskey improves with age," he said. "The older I get the better I like it."

CHAPTER 7

Gin, Vodka, Rum, and the Rest

HAVING LAID TO REST THE MYTH THAT GREAT AGE NECESSARILY improves all whiskey, we next shall explore gin, which normally is not aged at all. Most gin is pure alcohol, water, and flavoring, mainly with the fragrant essence of juniper berries, and it tastes somewhat the way Christmas trees smell. Its name comes from juniper, which the French call *genièvre,* spelled *juniver* by the Dutch, and shortened by the English to gin.

There are five kinds of gin (not counting sloe gin, which is not a gin at all, but one of the cordials described in the Appendix). Most people know only one kind—the "dry" gin that millions of Americans drink nearly straight under the pseudonym of a Martini cocktail. When you order gin, this is the kind you get.

Most dry gin has two confusing words on its label: "distilled," merely to distinguish it from the same product occasionally made by a compounding process, and "London," because this dry type first came from there. It is further confused by dry gins that are yellow, from brief aging, but which taste much the same as the white.

You can buy these dry gins at strengths ranging from 95 proof to as low as 80. Like whiskeys, American gins have tended since World War II to become less potent and less flavorful than formerly. Some brands have advertised their newly light taste, one even suggesting that its gin can now be drunk as a "naked Martini," thus ending forever the question of how much vermouth to add.

The other four kinds of gin are specialties not found in all stores; you might have to hunt for some of them.

One is Old Tom gin, which is merely sugar-syrup-sweetened instead of dry, and comes in handy for mixing a Tom Collins.

Another is Plymouth gin, traditionally halfway between the dry and Old Tom; in other words, slightly sweet. (However, I have tasted some in this country that was as dry as any from London.)

Then there is Hollands gin, also variously known as Dutch, Genever, Geneva, and Scheidam. It is so strongly grain-flavored, so pungent and aromatic of juniper and herbs, that although quite dry, it would ruin any cocktail. It can only be drunk straight, and at least one Genever label bluntly tells you so. In Holland, where gin originated, this type is the favorite "schnapps."

Finally, there are 70-proof flavored gins, assorted like the kinds of ice cream—orange, lemon, mint, raspberry, pineapple, grape, cherry, lime, chocolate—that have adherents in some localities, especially in the southern states.

Traditionally all gins contain, in addition to juniper, a number of aromatic herbs, seeds, and roots, such as coriander, angelica, cassia, anise, and fennel, but each is present in only a faint degree and cannot be recognized.

What most people ask me about gin is not how it tastes, but how it affects those who drink it. Aside from occasional allergy cases, which are another subject entirely, the most interesting thing about gin is that juniper oil is a diuretic—a powerful kidney stimulant. Whether there is enough of the oil in gin to produce this reaction in the average consumer does not seem to have been reported scientifically. It has been shown, however, that the neutral alcohol in gin hits the drinker faster than the more heavily flavored alcohol in whiskey does.

Gin is also rather interesting from social standpoints, because as a symbol of the drinker's status it has risen considerably over the years.

Early in the seventeenth century a Dutch professor named Sylvius discovered that the nauseous taste of the crudely distilled spirits of that era could be masked successfully with fragrant juniper berries and thereby made palatable. His creation, the original gin, became the poor people's tipple in the Netherlands.

When, some years later, England's "Good Queen Anne" raised the import duty on French light wines and lowered the tax on spirits, gin became the popular drink in Britain. An era of drunkenness followed, at the height of which an inn in Southwark displayed a sign, "Drunk for a penny; dead drunk for twopence; clean straw for nothing." Gin was called "royal poverty," because when beggars drank it they felt as great as kings. It took England two centuries to struggle back to sobriety.

In America gin was relatively an unimportant beverage, used primarily as an ingredient in some of the less powerful mixed drinks, until the prohibition era. That was when a generation of city dwellers bought alcohol from bootleggers and oil of juniper and glycerin from drugstores, and made bathtub gin the drink of the business classes. This white-collar connotation has stuck to gin ever since. And assisted no doubt by the growing potency of modern Martinis, juniper-flavored alcohol has become a symbol of Madison Avenue, of the professions, and of downtown drinkers everywhere.

Brandy for Gentlemen

When it comes to social status, no other distilled beverage has the prestige of brandy. For centuries while gin was "royal poverty," while rum was grog for sailors, and long before whiskey had attained genteel acceptance, brandy was the liquor of royalty and gentlemen. Its honored place at the climax of elegant banquets, where it is sipped undiluted from bulbous snifters, is shared with no other kind of spirit. And what else but brandy could possibly belong in the tiny wooden keg the noble Saint Bernard dog has borne through Swiss Alpine snowdrifts to revive and rescue lost travelers?

Because it is the distilled essence of wine—itself a potable liquid fermented from the juice of grapes—brandy has an intrinsic dignity that is lacking in liquors made from cooked mashes of grain or from mere molasses.

Its name began as *brandewijn* (burnt wine) in Dutch, becoming brandywine in English, and the Germans still call it *weinbrand.* To the French it is *eau de vie*—water of life—which, as we have seen, is also the original Celtic meaning of "whiskey."

Brandies, like whiskies and gins, come in several flavors. The most popular kind in this country simply calls itself brandy with no embellishing type description. If you find in small print on the label that it comes from California, you can expect the taste to be fruity, reminiscent of wine grapes, and slightly sweet. Various brands are drier, some are sweeter. Most are 84-proof blends of straight brandies two or more years of age, usually sweetened and smoothed with sugar and sherry. (Sometimes other smoothing agents, such as honey and fruit syrups, are used, too.)

Next there is cognac, the world-famous French specialty,

with its pronounced oily, somewhat soapy taste. It comes to the United States at 84 proof, often, in recent years, at 80. You either like cognac or you don't; as American tastes go, there seems no middle ground.

A third kind is also French. Its label merely says "imported French brandy, 84 proof." This is not cognac, and there is no predicting how it will taste, because the distillers of France apparently have not decided.

There are other kinds, not found everywhere. Some stores offer straight California brandies whose labels proclaim that they contain no flavoring, and in which you can taste the oak barrel. Some are bottled in bond, which means straight, unflavored, four or more years old, and 100 proof.

Occasionally you find armagnac, which resembles cognac but is usually more heavily flavored and tastes good only when drunk straight. Some expensive Spanish brandies remind you of old sherry. Pisco brandy from Peru, where it is called *aguardiente* (burning water) and which, with its spicy muscat grape flavor, makes the famous Latin-American drink called "Pisco sour," is also available in this country.

There is still another kind of brandy made from grapes, or rather from the pulp and seeds after the wine has been pressed. It is 100-proof grappa in Italy and America, *eau de vie de marc* in France. Colorless and fiery-tasting, grappa has its adherents in some neighborhoods.

As for fruit-flavored brandies, the kinds whose labels mention blackberry, apricot, peach, and cherry are not really brandies of those particular fruits. Instead, they usually are high-proof grape brandy with added flavoring of the fruits named. Look at the labels and you will see. They do not say "blackberry brandy," they say "blackberry-flavored brandy."

The true fruit brandies are applejack, which is apple

brandy; France's famous calvados (applejack distilled from hard apple cider in Normandy); kirschwasser (water of cherries), a brandy distilled from cherries; and slivovitz, a brandy distilled from plums, which usually tastes as though the plums had ripened too long.

Cognac is always praised as the peer of all brandies. The frills of cognac labeling with its stars, initials, and references to "Grande Champagne," "Petite Champagne" and "Fine Champagne" undeniably lend it glamour. Actually, whole constellations of stars are quite meaningless; "V.S.O." and "V.V.S.O.P." (see the Appendix for what they are supposed to mean) have no legal significance, and "Champagne" on a cognac label only represents a Frenchman's fancy that the soil of his neighborhood resembles that of Épernay or Reims, where bubbly wine is made.

No other brandy tastes just like cognac, and I happen to like it. However, mystery surrounds the source of its flavor. In the Charente and Charente Inférieure departments of France, which by French law are the only places where cognac can be made, they tell you its taste comes from the earth, the grapes, and pot-still distillation. Researchers from other countries have studied the Charentais methods and not all are convinced. They wonder how strictly France enforces its laws governing the purity of brandy, when there are hundreds of little distilleries to oversee. Their suspicion is heightened by the existence of a thriving trade in cognac oil, a flavoring made from the skins, pulp, and seeds of grapes. More than thirty thousand pounds of this oil are made in France in an average year. A few drops of it can make any brandy taste like cognac.

As for brandy's age, the facts are much like those about whiskeys: too much time spent in wood makes a liquor taste woody. And if anyone tries to sell you "Napoleon brandy," for which gullible Americans have paid fabulous sums, remember that even the French admit that no such liquor exists. It would have evaporated long ago.

Rum from Molasses

Because they are distilled mostly from fermented molasses, most rums have a molasses taste. Some have more, others have so little that they almost taste like brandy. But you virtually need a map of the West Indies to tell one rum from another, because a strange government regulation, born of international and insular politics, classifies rums not according to type, but according to their places of origin. Since some of the sugar islands produce assorted rum types, this results in a hodgepodge quite unintelligible to the average shopper, who has no guide to what the labels mean.

The only key to rum flavors I can suggest is that Cuban, Puerto Rican, Haitian, and Santo Domingo rums are mainly light in taste and color. Most of the rest—such as those from Barbados, Jamaica, Martinique, Trinidad, Virgin Islands—are usually (but not always) medium heavy to heavy, some as dark as molasses itself. Your choice among rums depends upon how you want to use them—in daiquiris, punches, flips or swizzles. I have tasted some Cuban brands so remarkably light and smooth that I could not believe they were rums at all until I learned that they were flavored with brandy, plums, raisins, and sherry wine. Your choice may also be influenced by price: Puerto Rican and Virgin Islands rums, because they enter this country free of import duties, are usually cheaper than products of foreign countries.

The strengths of rums vary from merely 80 proof all the way up to the fiery 151-proof Demerara rum, which is named for a river in British Guiana. I have read that this 151-proof spirit is drunk straight in northern climates by half-frozen lumberjacks who need thawing out. At such strength it would burn the roofs off their mouths; they surely must dilute it with something. This particular rum is one ingredient in the aptly named drink called a Zombie. Any liquor so potent, if used on flaming desserts or puddings, might well set your house afire. The 100-proof rums that are sold for this purpose are strong enough. And to make your Tom and Jerries you can buy ready-mixed 80.4-proof blends of medium-bodied rum and brandy.

Rums are made in any country where sugar cane grows, and not all of those sold in this country come from the Caribbean area. There is 100-proof Batavia arrack from Java, aromatic from palm wine toddy and from cooked, dried red Javanese rice. It is popular in Sweden as the base of Swedish *punsch*. This was the original rum of history, distilled continuously in the East Indies for twenty-eight centuries, and got its name from sweat—*araq* in Arabian.

We also have New England rums, moderately heavy and rummy. These date back to the notorious three-cornered rum and slave trade of colonial days, when molasses from the West Indies was distilled in New England, bartered in Africa for slaves, who then were sold in the West Indies for more molasses. New England rum had much to do with the Revolution, which resulted as much from England's import duty on molasses for distilling as from the tariff on tea.

How did rum, whose name suggests swashbuckling pirates and Caribbean calypso singers, acquire its inelegant title? Most writers credit it to England's Admiral Vernon, whose crews gave him two historic nicknames. One was "Old Rummy," and the watered spirits ration he gave his sailors became rumbullion or rumbustion, later shortened to rum (*ron* in Spanish, *rhum* in French). The other name they gave the admiral was "Old Grog" for the peculiar cloak he wore, made of a silk and mohair material called grogram. And according to legend, the rum-and-water potion that has been drunk daily by generations of English and Canadian seamen thus became known as grog.

Is Vodka Just Alcohol?

Have you ever stopped to consider what a difference a name makes? Whether you have or not, you might ask yourself this question: How many American men and women, of the millions who began drinking vodka between 1950 and 1960, would have done so if the labels on the bottles had read "alcohol" instead of "vodka"?

However you answer that one, which is pregnant with psychic nuances, it inevitably leads to the next: *Is* vodka merely plain alcohol?

Judge for yourself. One day six expert professional tasters gathered in a room to perform an experiment. Before each there were placed several code-numbered, unlabeled glasses. Half contained a well-known brand of 80-proof vodka. The other half held ordinary grain alcohol, diluted with distilled water from 190 proof down to the same strength as the vodka. The experts were asked to pick out the vodka. They sniffed, tasted, and spat, trying each sample repeatedly. Then the codes were unveiled. The result: all six experts had failed to tell vodka from plain alcohol.

I have since performed the same experiment in company with still another professional expert. We both failed the test, too, because vodka is nothing more nor less than watered alcohol.

But, you may protest, isn't vodka charcoal filtered, expensively processed as its glamorous advertising boasts? Doesn't that make it something entirely different from alcohol? No, it does not. Filtering might conceivably aerate a liquid, the way the gadget on your kitchen water faucet does, and the charcoal could remove impurities from something that is impure. But this alcohol before filtering is already quite pure. What the costly filtering does is to change alcohol's legal name. According to a 1949 government regulation, which accomplished this bit of semantical magic, the product before it is charcoal treated is alcohol (or its euphemistic legal nickname, "neutral spirits"). Percolate it through charcoal, which adds absolutely nothing, and presto! it is no longer alcohol; it has become vodka.

The government's official definition of vodka flatly states that it must be "without distinctive character, aroma, or taste." The ads boldly admit it: ". . . absolutely neutral" ". . . because it has no liquor taste or breath" ". . . loses itself completely in just about anything that pours" ". . . it leaves no whisper of liquor . . ." and ". . . never intrudes upon the flavor of your mixer."

In the strange story of vodka in America there are profound motivational problems to ponder. Perhaps they even offer some clues to the whole psychology of drinking.

Whatever you happen to drink, have you ever thought about why? If it is coffee, do you take it only for the stimulating effect of the drug caffeine it contains, or solely for its pleasing taste? If it is rye, do you seek the warm, burning feeling it gives going down, or do you merely want to be drunk? Is beer taken for thirst, for flavor, for mild alcoholic feeling, or for all of these things combined?

In vodka it cannot be taste, unless tomato juice tastes different in a Bloody Mary than when taken plain, or unless orange juice over ice acquires some new magic when added alcohol makes it a Screwdriver.

Or perhaps there is something symbolic involved, as in the religious uses of wine, or simply in the guilty knowledge that drinking any alcohol can be dangerous and is often forbidden.

One maker of wine and brandy posed the taste question puckishly in an advertisement: "If you can't see it, taste it or smell it, why bother?" he asked, going on to proclaim the toothsomeness of his own products which, he pointed out, "cannot be disguised by anything."

From the statistical position of a nonentity among spirits, colorless, tasteless, breathless, unaged vodka, at 80 and 100 proof, zoomed in a single decade to such popularity in America that it represented almost one tenth of all the distilled spirits drunk in the nation. "Ten years ago," a vodka marketer's ad boasted in 1959, "only one American in 1,000 had ever tasted vodka . . . [It] changed the drinking habits of a nation."

Vodka now even challenges whiskey and gin with a startling survey which shows, according to Smirnoff's John Martin, that 53.9 per cent of all the people who drink other distilled liquors admit in interviews that they do not like the taste of what they are drinking.

On a visit to New York I once mentioned Martin's survey to Samuel Bronfman, who as head of the House of Seagram has sold more whiskey than anyone else who ever lived. "If people don't like the taste of whiskey," America's whiskey king replied cheerfully, "it's funny that they drink two hundred million gallons of it in a year and pay up to twenty dollars a bottle for it!"

There is no question that vodka's "complete blendability" is an attraction to buyers, if only for its economy. From a single bottle you can mix a number of different kinds of drinks. You now can buy nonalcoholic flavors for all kinds of cocktails, from Martinis to Gimlets, at almost all drug and liquor stores. Several are made especially to be spiked with vodka. To the uninitiated, at least, the resulting mixed drinks resemble their genuine counterparts.

But is this tasteless American vodka the same as that drunk in Russia, where vodka was invented? Isn't the Russian kind distilled from potatoes, while the American is made entirely from grain?

The original Russian spirit came from various things—potatoes, grains, and whatever else was available—because alcohol can be made from almost anything, including sawdust and petroleum. When distilled at over 190 proof all spirits taste alike, anyway. It is true that Russia's early vodkas did have some character, mainly an unclean flavor because they were poorly distilled. The Cossacks used to mix their vodka with pepper to hide its nauseous taste. But when the Soviets embraced technology they developed vodkas fully as water white, pure, and tasteless, American travelers testify, as any in this country. Actually, "vodka" in Russia can mean any kind of ardent spirit, and there is more than one type. One is faintly sweet, reminiscent of rum. Another has an herb flavor from aromatic *zubrowka* (buffalo) grass steeped in the liquor. It is yellowish in color, and some bottles contain a straw of this grass. In other countries of eastern Europe this liquor is known as zubrowka, not as vodka. In Soviet Georgia there is a vodka that comes with whole peppers floating in the bottle.

What the Soviets usually drink as vodka is no stronger than the American kind. The bottle now usually reads "40%," which presumably means it is 80 proof, although some of 100 and 112 proof was sold as recently as 1950. What has spurred the Kremlin to clamp down on heavy drinking since Stalin's time is not vodka's present strength, but the way it is drunk —an entire 3½-ounce serving downed at a single gulp.

If quality in liquor means complete absence of flavor, American vodka is surely the best. At 80 proof, the strength at which most is sold here and in Canada, vodka is so smooth that a certain air-line steward has found an entirely new use for it. On long transpacific flights it solves his problem of how to handle obstreperous drunks. Instead of serving them a Scotch and water, he hands them a highball with vodka replacing the water. They soon pass out colder than from any pre-vodka Mickey Finn.

Perhaps the main effect vodka has had on American drinking is its influence on the flavors of other alcoholic beverages. Time was when the most prized liquors were those you could smell across a room. The popularity of vodka, which is the ultimate in blandness, has influenced the distillers of bourbon, Scotch, and gin to make their liquors lighter and lighter; and this trend is also evident in beer and wine.

Some blame the lightness trend not directly on vodka, but rather on the influence exerted by women, who lately have become important as liquor shoppers and as drinkers. This may well be where the credit belongs—or, if you miss the flavors drinks used to have—where the blame for liquor blandness lies.

You Can Buy the Real Stuff

Since vodka is just diluted alcohol, why not save money and buy it undiluted, under its own name? Perhaps you didn't know this (it is strange how few people know it), but the real stuff can be had. In more than half of our states you can buy bottled plain alcohol, labeled as such, in the same stores that sell vodka, whiskey, gin, brandy, and rum.

This alcohol will do everything 80-proof vodka does and more, because the kind that is sold is 190 proof, considerably more than twice as strong. Why pay for the water the distiller has added? Straight alcohol costs more per bottle, of course, because the federal tax on each kind of liquor is based on its proof, but by adding the water yourself you can get more than twice as much at diluted drinking strength, in relation to dollars expended.

However, there are some states—New York and California, for example—where alcohol cannot be bought without a doctor's prescription. Presumably the legislators of such states have decided in their wisdom that their constituents cannot be trusted with the genuine article, although they seemingly see nothing wrong with rum as potent as 151 proof. This situation is of considerable help to the bootleggers within their borders, who thereby enjoy a monopoly in the sale of non-prescription straight alcohol.

In the other states (populous Illinois, Pennsylvania, and Missouri are included, but see the Appendix section on Alcohol for a complete list), you can buy full-strength spirits with the same freedom that applies to less potent liquors. At one time stores in Kentucky stocked as many as ten competing alcohol brands, available in half pints, pints, fifths, quarts, and even gallons.

Since full-strength firewater would curdle your esophagus (so would 151-proof rum, for that matter), who buys it? I am told that the principal customers are those foreign born who require for ceremonial uses, or for plain imbibing, certain traditional mixtures that are occasionally imported but not available everywhere. Peppermint schnapps, various Chinese liquors, and the Greeks' favorite masticha are examples. It is also reported that some fabulously hearty drinkers in northern states drink grape juice spiked with this alcohol, a taste they acquired during prohibition.

I, for one, see nothing immoral in do it yourself applied to the fine art of concocting beverages with tax-paid alcohol. A neighbor of mine in California, who gets his fully taxed spirits from a druggist friend, makes and ages in his cellar the best peach liqueur I have ever tasted anywhere. Old-time recipe books, which you can find in secondhand bookstores, contain scores of recipes for such potables. That famed connoisseur, Dr. Charles Pierre Mathé, once let me sample his exotic Liqueur de la Pendule and gave me his wonderful recipe, which calls for suspending an orange in a sealed bottle, in which the alcohol, without ever touching the fruit, extracts the essence of its delicate flavor.

No other solvent but high-proof alcohol can extract and dissolve in a completely cloudless liquid the essential flavoring oils of fruits and herbs. This is why the lemon extract in your kitchen contains 80 per cent alcohol, and why so many medicines are alcohol solutions. Alcohol is so efficient as a flavor *solvent* that there may even be an excuse for vodka.

In some parts of Canada this matter of buying plain alcohol is considerably simpler than in the United States. In Québec, Ontario, New Brunswick, and Prince Edward Island provinces you can buy it as such, already diluted to vodka strength.

The Ontario Liquor Control Board, for example, the last time I checked, was selling bottles of 80-proof alcohol for a whole dollar less than the cheapest vodka or gin. While eight other Canadian states confined alcohol sales to physicians and others with special permits, Québec faced the issue the most squarely of all. The Commission des Liqueurs de Québec simply refused to sell anything labeled as vodka. It sold 80-proof *"alcool,"* also called "Whiskey Blanc," instead.

Regional Potations

The people of every land drink whatever liquors can be made from whatever happens to grow there. And since America's great melting pot has not yet finished cooking its people into a uniform mass, there still are local preferences for a number of spirits besides those I have described.

Aquavit, the white lightning of Scandinavia, is still swallowed at a gulp by many residents of northern states, accompanied by this hearty toast: *"Min skaal, din skaal, alla vackra flickornas skaal,"* which pledges your health, my health, and all the pretty girls' health. This kind of liquor is basically like Hollands gin, except that it is flavored with caraway seed instead of with juniper berries. An ounce of ice-cold aquavit, followed by a beer chaser, is the traditional prelude to many a Scandinavian meal.

The increasing numbers of Americans who vacation in old Mexico have brought home a taste for tequila, the water-white spirit distilled from fermented juice of the cactus variety we call century plant. Mexicans drink it in the following manner: First sprinkle salt on thumbnail or wrist. Next tilt back head, squeeze fresh lime juice on tongue. Now toss salt into mouth, to strike tongue. Then toss in tequila, and swallow. This strenuous method of disguising tequila's taste has not followed it north of the border. Instead, we have the tequila Martini, which merely requires a salted lemon slice in the cocktail. At last reports sales of tequila, at 80 and 86 proof, were soaring.

Since romantic Hawaii is now a state, this compendium cannot omit okolehao, the island liquor commonly called for as "oke." Either white or smoky in color, okolehao has a pronounced flavor of the ingredients from which it is distilled: the juice of baked ti root (the taro plant that makes Hawaiian poi), Koji rice, and molasses.

In the Chinatowns of American cities you find a number of weird spirit and herb concoctions, some of which taste like the modern celestial's answer to the ancients' cup of hemlock. The most popular is ng ka pei, sometimes referred to as Chinese whiskey. I rather like it, but having once served this liquor straight at the close of an authentic Chinese banquet, which I arranged for the Wine and Food Society, I must caution the reader not to expect enthusiastic acceptance of ng ka pei by his American guests. Try it sometime in a Chinatown bar and you will see what I mean.

Speaking of regional liquors, it is worth mentioning that the leading American spirit, bourbon, is still little known outside of North America. Admiral William J. Marshall, president of the Bourbon Institute, has set out on a campaign to remedy this situation, and has even held bourbon tastings in Scotch-soaked Britain. The admiral has also made a driblet of progress in France. Among the French, following World War II, a snobbish trend had made whiskey briefly popular until the cognac distillers awakened to the threat. They soon prevailed upon their government to make the American product a "nonessential" import that France must do without. In

1959, in response to United States Government pressure generated by the Bourbon Institute, France officially lifted its whiskey import restrictions—but refused to allow any distilled liquor except cognac to be advertised.

In America, the most remarkable thing in regional liquor tastes is the liking for brandy in Wisconsin. There one out of every five bottles of liquor drunk is brandy, compared to one bottle out of forty in the nation as a whole. Nobody in the liquor industry has yet been able to figure out why this is so in Wisconsin but nowhere else. The distillers of brandy hopefully look to Wisconsin as portending a future national trend.

CHAPTER 8

Highballs, Cocktails, Shots, and Elixirs

How do you choose, when the host asks "what'll yours be?" among highballs, cocktails, "on the rocks," or straight shots? If you wonder about the different ways to take distilled liquors, here are some facts that may help to guide you.

Medical authorities agree that any drink stronger than 20 per cent alcohol by volume irritates your throat and gizzard. (From 15 to 20 per cent there is slight irritation; below 10 per cent there is none.) They especially condemn the time-honored American custom of gulping whiskey neat. They say this causes chronic gastritis and "the American disease," dyspepsia.

The more you dilute your liquor with water or other mix, the longer you normally take to drink it. Some of the spirit is being oxidized in your body before you have finished drinking the rest. Besides, no matter how fast you drink, a jigger of whiskey in a highball does not raise the alcohol content of your blood as high as when the same amount of liquor is taken straight. The result is that you feel less intoxicating "kick" from the highball; an even, pleasant glow is felt, and you are less apt to become drunk from a couple of before-dinner drinks.

When a straight shot is followed by a water chaser, the liquor is diluted in the stomach, but the tissues have already been irritated. Liquor "on the rocks" is less intoxicating than a shot, not because the melting ice dilutes it very much, but only because the drink is taken slowly.

Sweet mixes and the sugar used in such mixtures as Collinses and sours slightly reduce the wallop of these drinks, because any increase in the sugar content of your blood modifies the effect of alcohol. On the other hand, sparkling water may possibly increase the "kick" a little. Some authorities believe the bubbles of carbon dioxide speed the absorption of alcohol into the blood stream, but final proof of this is lacking.

The long and short of all this seems to be that the more you dilute your drinks—whatever you use to dilute them—the better for both your health and your behavior.

But don't reverse the mix and the liquor, as I found one of my bibulous friends doing at a convention recently. He ordered a half-glass of milk, then signaled the bartender to fill the rest of the glass with whiskey. "It's a Scotch cow," he explained. "Doctor's orders—milk for my ulcer, you know. Of course the doc didn't say not to put Scotch in it."

Do strong drinks lead to problem drinking? Since it usually takes several years of excessive drinking to develop dependence on alcohol, it is clear that the stronger beverages at least tend to speed the process. "If all whiskey were diluted down to highball concentration," the late Professor Yandell Henderson of Yale wrote in 1935, "the liquor problem would be diminished even more than in proportion to the dilution."

Professor Henderson calculated normal highball strength at 15 to 20 per cent alcohol. He objected to cocktails because of their potency (nowadays 25 to 40 per cent) and the rapidity with which they are often swallowed, usually on an empty stomach. He lauded the European custom of drinking light table wine with meals, but, doubting whether Americans would ever become wine drinkers, Henderson wound up recommending 5 per cent beer.

Lewis S. Rosenstiel, boss of the vast Schenley liquor empire, agrees that long drinks are more temperate than short ones. He long has advocated legislation that would enable distillers to bottle and sell an 11 per cent carbonated highball. "Besides, we can make a better highball than the consumer can," he says. In 1933 Rosenstiel even organized a company to turn out such a drink, and lost a fortune because he could not get the law changed to make it inexpensive.

There are bottled highballs on the market now, but the tax burden they carry has kept them in the luxury class. Bottled premixed cocktails, on the other hand, are at the height of their popularity, because of the considerable labor and care they save. But don't serve them undiluted from their bottles as some railroad club-car stewards do, because the popular brands come at 60 to 75 proof (30 to 37½ per cent alcohol), which is slightly stronger than the average bartender's mixture. Stir or shake them with plenty of ice, as the labels specify. (Air lines serve premixed cocktails, too, but theirs are especially bottled at "banquet strength," 48 to 55 proof, and are usually served chilled in miniature bottles, undiluted.)

The word "cocktail" means a short iced drink of spirituous liquor with flavoring ingredients. It got its name during the Revolution, a popular legend says, when Betsy Flannagan, the proprietress of the Four Corners Inn near Tarrytown, served Washington's officers a round of her mixed bracers, each decorated with the tail feathers of a rooster. On that occasion a young French officer in the group is supposed to have uttered these immortal words: *"Vive le cocktail!"*

The origin of America's most popular cocktail, the Martini,

has been traced by various historians to France, Italy, Boston (where they called it a Martingale), and New Orleans (where it was called a Martineau). But the strongest evidence credits the Martini's creation to "Professor" Jerry Thomas, principal bartender at the Metropolis Hotel in New York, who also served briefly in a San Francisco saloon. Thomas published in 1862 a book of his 306 original recipes, including the Tom and Jerry, the Blue Blazer, and this one, which he called the "Martinez cocktail":

> 1 dash bitters, 2 dashes maraschino, 1 pony of Old Tom gin, 1 wineglass of vermouth, 2 small lumps of ice. Shake up thoroughly and strain into a large cocktail glass. Put a quarter-slice lemon in the glass and serve. If the guest prefers it very sweet add 2 dashes gum syrup.

Since a pony is one ounce, and the wineglass measure is two ounces, this means that the original Martini contained two parts of vermouth to one part of gin, not the ten of gin to one of vermouth often drunk in the United States today. Moreover, the "Professor's" gin was sweet, his drink was shaken, not stirred, and his other ingredients help to present a sharp contrast to the other recipes often offered as the "classic" Martini.

Despite such evidence, the battle over how little vermouth traditionally belongs in a Martini continues to rage unchecked. It has become an endless serial-type joke, with such variants as the shadow Martini, in which the vermouth bottle is only allowed to cast its shadow on the glass, and the whisper Martini, in which the bartender leans over the mixing glass and gently speaks the word "vermouth." Meanwhile, drinkers strive to impress one another by insisting, "Make the next one a little drier, please."

A recent casualty in some localities is the olive, banished because it displaces 1/17 of the liquid, and succeeded by the onion, which displaces only 1/57 and thereby transforms the drink into a Gibson. Even those who relish the civilizing influence of vermouth have gone along with the gag, grinning sheepishly as they order "a wet Martini." But all such jokes must reach an end. This may have occurred when women began saying, "Give me a Gibson without the onion—and no vermouth," which is using many words to order a glass of gin.

It is high time for drinkers to recognize that an "extra dry" Martini is not a cocktail; it is straight gin.

American fads in mixed drinks, like fads in dress, cars, and amusements, continually sweep across the land, some helped by artful promotion, as of lime juice which, when mixed with gin or vodka and ice, becomes a Gimlet. Vodka first floated into popularity with a drink called a Moscow Mule, followed by the Screwdriver. Taste appeal, which might be expected to favor sweet, aromatic concoctions, often is not even secondary. More powerful influences than taste in choice among drinks are prestige among fellow drinkers and the imagined differences in aftereffects, about which the truth is told in the chapters on fables and hangover.

Such considerations have less influence in the older countries, where alcoholic beverages have long been taken for granted. The Frenchman and the Italian still calmly sip their apéritifs, diluted liberally with seltzer, having selected each drink for its flavor and for the appetite and digestion-promoting qualities it is believed to possess. Wine is the European mealtime beverage, beer is drunk freely, and the cordials and liqueurs, which as yet are little used in America, are appreciated for the gracious finishing touch they give to fine dinners.

This book is neither a bartending guide nor a drink encyclopedia. Thousands of enticing recipes and the vast numbers of apéritifs and liqueurs are well described in so many chock-full volumes that a collection of the best ones would constitute a whole library. In the South there are scores of different juleps, all made with sprigs of mint, but none resembles the original version, which was made from ale, honey, and spices, and named for the Persian *gulab,* which only means "a sweet drink." Originally from Spain came the sangarees, named for blood (*sangre*); a hotel in Singapore created the sling, and the swizzles, named for the swizzle stick used to stir and make them frosty, began in the West Indies. But their original basic ingredients have been so shuffled and varied that nobody can claim any longer that his recipe is authentic, unless it is one he invented himself.

The best recipe advice to the home bartender is to measure liquor carefully; don't confuse generosity with hospitality. Besides, exact measurement insures success every time. If you aren't particularly ambitious, use the recipe booklets most liquor stores offer; buy your Tom and Jerry and eggnog basics from your dairy, and remember these three things: have plenty of ice on hand, stir or shake drinks well to get them diluted, and have soft drinks available for the guest who doesn't drink.

There is much to be said for the bitters, apéritifs, and elixirs popular in Europe. The best known of these continental favorites are described individually in the Appendix, but the main characteristics of these kinds of drinks are worth discussing here.

Medical research in modern times has proved that some bitter substances have the power to stimulate appetite, but the Europeans who drink bitter apéritifs before their meals knew it long ago. Alcoholic bitters in concentrated form can be bought for the flavoring of cocktails, and are also sold as medicines. Their formulas are proprietary secrets, but angostura bark and quinine, the bitter white alkaloid from the bark of cinchona trees, are known to be included in some.

Europe's traditional apéritif drinks, such as byrrh, Dubonnet, St. Raphael, and campari, are aromatized wines containing the bitter principle. So, for that matter, are vermouths, which are popular on the Continent as before-meal drinks.

Apéritif in French means both an appetizer and a gentle laxative, but there is no evidence that the drinks in question have the latter quality. What is puzzling, however, is that both alcohol and sugar, which are present in all of these apéritifs, are actually killers of appetite. Whether the bitterness of the drinks is enough to make the imbibers hungry while their alcohol and sugar works in the opposite way does not seem to have been determined.

The elixirs known as cordials or liqueurs (modern usage has made these two terms synonymous) trace their origins to the alchemists of the Middle Ages, the monks in flowing robes who sought by stirring liquids in strange vessels and retorts to find the elixir of life. Many were accused of sorcery and black magic, and some were even executed. ("Elixir" is from the Arabic name for the philosophers' stone, *El-Iksir.* The word now only means a strong extract or tincture.) The alchemists hoped to transmute base metals into gold and to find the universal cure for all diseases, to prolong life indefinitely. What they produced, instead, were medicines. For the original cordials (from the Latin *cor* or *cordis,* signifying heart) were intended as heart stimulants and as love potions.

The elixirs they called liqueurs were also originally medicinal preparations. *(Liqueur,* in French, simply means "liquor.") The French call them *digestifs,* because all of these drinks contain essential oils which, if taken in moderate doses, are believed to relieve some of the distressed feeling that comes from overeating. Many of their individual ingredients have acknowledged medicinal properties, evidenced by their listings in the pharmacopoeia.

Liqueurs (the word more commonly used) are now mainly served, as the Benedictine advertisement puts it, to "finish dinner with a flourish." They also appear in numerous cocktail recipes, in which they were popular during prohibition to cover the raw taste of bootleg spirits; are often drunk as highballs, and have many uses in cooking, especially to flavor desserts.

The extraction of ethereal flavors from hundreds of herbs, fruits, peels, berries, seeds, roots, leaves, and flowers can only be accomplished by alcohol; and most liqueurs, although regarded as ladies' drinks, are alcoholically potent. They range from 50 proof (anisette and crème de cacao) to green chartreuse at 110. The principal spirits used are water-white, neutral grape brandies.

All liqueurs are sweet. In fact, the United States Government requires a product to contain at least 2½ per cent sugar by weight if it is to be labeled as a liqueur or cordial. This amounts to approximately one and a half tablespoons of simple syrup per quart. Most of them also contain glycerin, which, when you take too much of it, can make you remarkably uncomfortable.

Many of the recipes are secrets, jealously guarded by their makers for centuries. Green chartreuse is said to contain 230 distinct elements; yellow chartreuse, 120. But some are relatively simple, and old-fashioned housewives used to brew them in their kitchens. (But no liqueur is simpler than the half pints of "bourbon liqueur" and "rye liqueur" sold in New York. These sweetened whiskies have come into being solely because the New York law has a quirk prohibiting the sale of whiskey in half-pint bottles.)

Secret recipes contain no mysteries, however, for modern flavor chemists, and Europe no longer has a monopoly on the manufacture of liqueurs. All countries have equal access to the ingredients, which are gathered from all over the world. Virtually all of the Old World elixirs are now duplicated in the United States, and many of the American products, with the advantages of superior fruits and equipment, are probably better than the European originals. But because many of the best-known liqueur names are proprietary possessions of the makers in France, Italy, Denmark, and other countries, the American counterparts of these have not yet gained recognition. In a few instances the names and formulas have been purchased by American companies. Imported liqueurs whose names are not proprietary (such as anisette, curaçao, crème de menthe, and kümmel) have no advantages over the American versions. This country also has its own original elixirs (Rock and Rye, Forbidden Fruit, and Southern Comfort, for example), some of which are exported to other countries.

Homemade liqueurs have been popular for centuries, and you can make your own at home if you can get some full-strength alcohol (see the Appendix for the list of states where it can be purchased). Instructions are given in old books of recipes. Flavoring ingredients are available from your grocer, from herb dealers, or from your garden.

One of the simplest to prepare at home is a crude version of crème de menthe. A friend of mine makes his from equal parts of simple syrup, alcohol, and water, to which he adds mint extract and green vegetable coloring, both of the latter bought at his neighborhood food store. His recipe calls for one-half teaspoon of mint extract per quart. You also can experiment with 100-proof vodka, adding herbs or peels and sugar to the partly-filled bottle and letting them soak for a day or two. But to extract such flavors fully you really need 190-proof alcohol.

Don't try to make absinthe. This greenish elixir with a dry, bitter licorice-like flavor has a reputation so wicked that its sale has been prohibited in France, the United States, and in most other Western countries.

Invented late in the eighteenth century by a French doctor living in Switzerland, absinthe became the drink of fast-living Frenchmen, who called it The Green Muse. A strange ritual was observed by its users: First the liquor was poured into a tall glass. Then, through a perforated absinthe spoon containing a lump of sugar, cold water was added, a single drop at a time. If the water was poured quickly, the liquor remained green, but when added drop by drop, it turned the absinthe a cloudy yellow, and the taste was just right.

The dissipations of French absinthe drinkers have been dramatized lately in the filmed story of Toulouse-Lautrec, the artist of the Moulin Rouge, who drank himself to madness and death at the age of thirty-seven. So many others became insane, and so many deaths were blamed on this liquor, that France, fearing a drop in the nation's birth rate, outlawed the genuine absinthe in 1914.

Some authorities have maintained that the damage to absinthe's victims resulted only from the liquor's original strength, 136 to as high as 161 proof. But pharmacologists believe the real cause of trouble was a narcotic substance called thujone or absinthol, contained in oil of wormwood, the essence of the original absinthe, and that the massive doses of the essence in so powerful an alcoholic drink caused the hallucinations, convulsions, and mania of absinthism. This need not cause the slightest alarm among the people who buy wormwood at health food stores to brew old-fashioned bitter wormwood tea at home, or who drink wormwood-flavored medicines and liquors. The wormwood shrub itself contains so little of the oil (less than ½ of 1 per cent) that they would have to take gallons of such liquids to get any absinthol effect. Actually, both wormwood and its oil have long-established medicinal values.

Absinthe's flavor, required in some Sazerac cocktails and in the original recipe for Oysters Rockefeller, is still available in substitutes. Anisette liquors, which taste like licorice but lack its bitterness, have replaced The Green Muse in virtually all countries.

Returning to the sweet liqueurs, a point worth considering is that their principal use is after meals. Because the food already taken delays the absorption of alcohol, these drinks are not especially intoxicating, although all of the alcohol you drink eventually gets into your blood.

But before-meal drinking is another matter entirely. Cocktails are under attack nowadays because of the time at which they are mainly drunk. The cocktail hour, an American custom that is fast spreading to other countries, is widely condemned because many an afternoon drinker, fatigued, nerve-frazzled, and starved for food, deliberately seeks alcoholic effect. Drs. Giorgio Lolli, Emidio Serianni, and associates, in a Yale publication on alcohol in Italian culture, say of the cocktail hour that "if a social institution had been consciously created to foster the development of latent alcohol-addictive traits, it is difficult to imagine how a more effective mechanism could have been devised."

On the other hand, Dr. Harry J. Johnson of New York,

president of the Life Extension Foundation, having studied the health examinations of 6,000 executives, defends one cocktail before dinner as "good medicine for the healthy executive [because] it settles him down, relaxes him." Dr. Johnson levels his fire, instead, at the lunchtime cocktail, indulged in by one tenth of the executives examined. He says a midday drink slows down physical activity, preventing the drinker from getting the exercise he needs to relieve his emotional stress and to keep him healthy. The lunchtime cocktail, he insists, "should be eliminated completely; it serves no earthly purpose, and it actually interferes with mental efficiency in the afternoon."

CHAPTER 9

Beer Benign

ABOUT EIGHTY-FIVE MILLION BOTTLES, CANS, AND GLASSES OF beer are consumed in the United States during an average day. Yet those who drink this beverage know surprisingly little about it.

For example, few of the more than fifty-four million Americans who enjoy beer know what theirs is made of, how much alcohol it contains, why some people put salt in it, or what is the difference between draught and bottled or canned beers. Some consumers may think they know these things, but with rare exceptions they do not.

What they do know is that this sudsy liquid is cool, tangy, and thirst-quenching, and that it relaxes but seldom intoxicates them. This is not surprising, since most beer is 91 per cent water; 4½ per cent is cereal substances, sugar, and bubbles of foam, while only 4½ per cent, on the average, is alcohol. Incidentally, the water content has been rising in recent years and the solid substances have been dropping—which helps explain why beer no longer has the flavor it had a generation ago.

Beer is a fermented drink. Prehistoric man undoubtedly discovered it, as he discovered wine, purely by accident. Juices of fruits, grains, leaves, roots, tree saps, and honey can ferment without human help and make an alcoholic drink. No country can claim to have invented beer, because it has been invented everywhere.

Nowadays beer is a cereal beverage. Barley malt, rice, and corn are brewed (which means boiled); their juices are flavored with the flowers of the hop vine to give them bitterness, then fermented, aged several weeks, and usually carbonated with the same gas released during their fermentation. Unlike the spirituous beverages, such as whiskey, whose alcohol has been concentrated by distillation, beer contains only the alcohol formed by natural fermentation. Made from grains not unlike those that make bread, and possessing food value (about 230 calories per pint), beer is sometimes described as "liquid bread."

Beer is many things to many people. It is the chief drink poured in British pubs, American taverns, and baseball parks; the key to drinking fellowship among college students; the sole exhilarating beverage millions of servicemen knew in hundreds of wartime outposts; the convenient cold drink on innumerable summer picnics; the traditional companion of hot dogs and *Bratwurst,* and an ingredient in some kinds of cookery. In the German beer gardens whole families listen to music, eat, and drink a liter of beer from a single family glass.

To workers in the brewery, beer is nourishment. Long before coffee breaks were ever thought of in other industries, brewers had their "beer times" on the job. To this day, nearly every brewers' union contract specifically requires the employer to supply his "good product" to employees once during the morning shift, once at midday, once in the afternoon, and once at quitting time, with no limits specified as to quantity.

The brewing industry calls it "the friendly beverage," often trying to associate beer with aristocratic society. But its modest price deprives it of snob appeal and keeps beer, with the exception of the costly imports, at the social level of the masses.

Three types of beer are generally sold in this country. First is the pale golden kind simply labeled as beer; this is the type known as lager. Second, there is ale, a kind of beer that is usually darker, stronger, and more bitter. Third is the new sort called "malt liquor." There are other brews, too: bock, dark draught beer, stock ale, stout, and porter, which are specialties not available everywhere; the flavored beers, drunk in Germany; mead, fermented from honey; Mexico's pulque, and Japanese sake. All of them will be described presently.

Most American beer is lager, a word from the German *lagern,* "to store," or, more simply, means aged. It is light-bodied, fresh-tasting, and faintly bitter from hops. Some brewers also call theirs Pilsner type, for the famed lager beer of Pilsen in Bohemia.

Today's American ales, although hoppier and heavier than lagers, are much milder-tasting than the "mild and bitter" that is the national drink of Britain. Ale was the brew drunk in America's colonial days, because it was brought to this country from England; the Pilgrims carried a liberal stock on the *Mayflower.* John Alden, who wooed Priscilla, was a cooper by trade, and came along on the voyage to take care of the barrels. The lager-beer type began to displace ale in the United States during the nineteenth-century German migration. Little ale is drunk by Americans now, although it still holds first rank in eastern Canada. The national Canadian trend, however, is toward lager.

The dividing line between beer and ale is that lager beer is "bottom-fermented" (the yeast settles to the bottom of the tank during fermentation) while ale is "top-fermented" (the yeast floats at the top). But some breweries make their ale by the bottom-fermentation method, too; and anyway, what interests the drinker is the drink, not how it is made. Those who want a more bitter, fuller-bodied, stronger drink than beer are likely to get it by buying ale.

"Malt liquors" are relative newcomers in the assortment of brewed drinks. The "malt" in their name is misleading; it does not mean they contain any more malt than beer does; they are likely to contain less. They have less beery taste than lagers or ales, and very little foam. Some are entirely new, bold ventures in beverage flavor. Certain "malt liquors," mainly packaged in cans and sold in liquor stores, are nearly double the strength of light beer, and advertise that they are "strong." In fact, some products of this group exist primarily because certain states have laws setting maximum alcohol contents for "beer" but have no such limits for "malt liquor."

This leads to the question perennially argued about beer: is it intoxicating? To answer it, we first must consider its alcoholic content.

Compared to the distilled liquors of 25 to 75½ per cent alcohol, the average 4½ per cent strength of American beers seems insignificant and even innocuous. Nevertheless, the debate about beer's potency continues, kept alive partly by the prohibitionists, who see a devil lurking in every drop, partly by liquor-soaked drivers who tell the police they "only had a couple of beers," and also by the confusion that surrounds the actual alcoholic content of each bottle, can, or keg.

Several states prohibit any statement of alcoholic strength from appearing on beer labels, while a number of other states specifically require it. (Both kinds of regulations presumably are intended to promote moderation.) Some states have different tax rates for beers of different strengths and different regulations governing their distribution.

The brewers contribute to the muddle. Whenever they

state alcoholic content, they express it in percentage of the liquid's weight. This confuses and misleads the consumer, because alcoholic content by volume (the figure given on wine labels and the basis of the "proof" statements on spirits) is actually one fourth greater than content by weight. Brewers defend their "by weight" custom, insisting it is more precise than "by volume." Perhaps this practice, in which 4 per cent beer is called "3.2 per cent by weight," helps the brewing industry in its campaigns for reasonable taxation and regulation. But it has not worked very well, if the 2.7-cent tax burden now loaded on the average glass of beer in this country is any indication.

In this book all beverage strengths are stated either in percentage by volume or in American proof, which translates to the same thing.

Actually, American lager beers range from 3.87 to 6.2 per cent in alcohol by volume. (The latter is a specialty found only in Minnesota.) The leading national brands vary mainly from 4 to 5 per cent, but stay slightly under 4 in those states where stronger beer is legally restricted in various ways. American ales vary from 5 to 5.6 per cent in the East and Midwest, but go as high as 7.5 per cent on the Pacific Coast. The brews labeled "malt liquor," exempt from states' maximums applicable to "beer," have been shown in tests to contain from 5.4 to more than 7 per cent alcohol. In Canada, lager beers test from 3.8 to 5.1 per cent, ales from 4.7 to 5.7; Canada has no "malt liquors."

Beers imported from foreign countries are often stronger than those made here, but the importers are careful to keep them under the maximum strengths permissible in individual states. Imported ales and stouts vary widely; some are under 4 per cent alcohol, while others go as high as 8 per cent.

To help you know the alcoholic content of the beer sold where you live, the Appendix contains a condensed summary of those states' regulations that set permissible strengths for malt beverages sold within their borders.

Impartial researchers in several different American institutions have tested beers of average strength in experiments on human subjects, to determine whether beer is intoxicating. They first carefully explain what they mean by intoxication: the concentration of .15 per cent alcohol in the blood, the figure legally recognized in most states as meaning that a person is drunk.

To reach the .15 per cent blood-alcohol level, they find, a drinker must swallow more than 2½ quarts of 4½ per cent beer in a matter of minutes. Since the capacity of the normal human stomach is between 1½ and 2 quarts, this feat is well-nigh impossible for an average man.

In a classic test performed at the University of Chicago in 1934, twenty-nine men and women actually tried to down twenty-one bottles of 4 per cent beer each, nearly two gallons, in 3½ hours. The scene must have been like a page from Rabelais. All of the subjects suffered nausea and vomiting, and among the few who succeeded for the sake of science, only five reached the legal level of intoxication.

The researchers' answer, then, to the question of whether beer is an intoxicating beverage is that it depends on what you mean by intoxication: that if you mean the grossly abnormal condition that American courts legally classify as drunkenness, it cannot be produced in a normal person with ordinary beer. (They do not say this of the stronger beers.)

This equivocal pronouncement does not hold water, if I may use an inappropriate phrase, when the issue is simply whether beer can make you gay, giddy, happy, high, or mellow—some of the scores of English expressions that mean you are slightly under the influence of alcohol. These milder forms of inebriation are easily achieved with 4½ per cent beer. Even one bottle poured into an empty stomach has been known to make a drinker dizzy, and four bottles consumed in a short time make it unsafe for an individual to drive.

The seemingly endless debate on this fuzzy subject could easily be resolved if the contending factions would only take advantage of the alcoholic slang in which our language is remarkably rich. Surely they could agree that beer can get you high, but that it is unlikely to get you soused.

All of the foregoing discussions may seem pointless to the average drinker of foamy brew, because he well knows the truth of the jingle which says that for anyone who wants to be drunk, "licker is quicker." Ask him why he chooses beer, and he gives you several different answers: he is thirsty, or he likes the taste, or it makes him feel good, or he considers it healthful, or he wants to lose weight, or he wants to gain weight, or he simply cannot explain.

Researchers have long sought to determine the basic underlying motives that account for the use of alcoholic beverages in all cultures and all nations over thousands of years. There are numerous theories as to why people drink strong beverages and make themselves drunk. An entirely separate question is why many more millions continually drink the milder beverages, which do not intoxicate them, with no intention of getting drunk. The scientists now believe the latter has something to do with mankind's need for relief from emotional tension and stress.

This was only conjecture until researchers at Yale University undertook in 1956 a series of experiments to test the tension and stress theory on beer, followed by tests on wine.

The scientists began their tests with animals. They first annoyed a group of rats by ringing a bell loudly at intervals outside the animals' cages. The noise made the creatures frantic; they raced around in circles, refused to eat, and became neurotic. Then the animals were fed measured amounts of alcohol, the doses corresponding to one, two, or three bottles of beer consumed by an average human. One bottle reduced their agitated behavior by 40 per cent. Two bottles reduced it by half. After doses equivalent to three bottles, the rats no longer paid any attention to the bell. They merely wiggled their whiskers and nibbled their food serenely.

Next came tests on human beings. Volunteers were made jittery by electric shocks and by loud blasts of a horn. Tension and stress were measured by the resistance of the subjects' skin to the passage of an electric current. (An agitated person's skin readily conducts electricity; a calm person's skin has higher resistance. Through electrodes attached to the soles of the subjects' feet their skin-conductance levels were registered automatically on a chart.)

Half a bottle of beer decreased basal tension by an average of 13 per cent, and emotional response to a sudden stress was reduced by 8 per cent. Two bottles reduced basal tension by 37 per cent and stress response by 50 per cent. Meanwhile, equal numbers of "control" subjects took the same tests, but the beer they were given contained no alcohol; it was near-beer. The nonalcoholic beer relaxed the "control" subjects only slightly.

(How wine fared in similar tests is told in the following chapter.)

The researchers' conclusion is that human beings need a periodic respite from emotional tension, and that the mild sedative action of beer and wine, when used in moderation, relieves the minor anxieties, resentments, fears, and frustrations that accumulate during an ordinary day. In other words, to borrow a word from an especially prosperous branch of the drug business, these beverages are now pictured as benign natural tranquilizers.

Perhaps this motive for drinking beer explains why it manages to retain its rank as the third leading beverage, next to milk and coffee, in America. Some such explanation is needed, because–compared to the hearty, malty, bitter beer people quaffed in our grandfathers' era—the average American beer today is watery, bland, sweet, and insipid.

What has happened to beer flavor? For one thing, the bitterness is nearly gone. The characteristic bitter beery flavor of beer comes from hops—from the yellow powder called lupulin contained in the flowers of the female hop vine. In 1934 the average American beer was made with 70 pounds of hops per hundred barrels. In 1949 the average use of hops had dropped to 44 pounds, and by 1959 it had fallen below 32.5 pounds—less than half the amount used in old-fashioned beer. This trend away from bitter beer inspired one brewery some years ago to advertise "Just the kiss of the hops–none of the bitterness," a slogan which a radio announcer once tongue-twisted to "the hiss of the cops." Since the ad was conceived, many other beers have overtaken the brand in question in the industry-wide rush toward blandness.

At the same time, the body–the substance, the nourishing food solids content—of beer has also declined. The body originally came from the malt (sprouted barley) of which beers were mainly made in earlier days. The use of malt in American breweries has declined almost one fourth (from 38.1 pounds per barrel to less than 29 pounds) since 1934. Other grains, principally corn and rice, which the brewers call "adjuncts," have replaced the missing malt, but only partly. For the total cereal solids content of beer, which provides its protein and other food values, is approximately one seventh less nowadays than it used to be.

Old-time brewers and lovers of flavorful old-fashioned beers mourn the blandness trend. They see the stratospheric rise of imported beers (up 400 per cent in sales since 1937 despite prices almost double those of American brands) as one result. Some blame today's bland beer for the decline in per-capita beer consumption from 18.4 gallons in 1947 to 15 gallons in 1958. Undoubtedly it is largely responsible for the nationwide revival of illegal home-brewing.

Heavy-bodied beers are more temperate than the bland type. The more food solids a beer contains, the slower its alcohol is absorbed into your blood stream. And the more flavor it has, the less you are likely to drink; a couple of beers will fill you up.

"The public is responsible for light-bodied beer," one brewmaster complained to me. "The way they buy the kind without flavor, you'd think they were going to drink it with ice cream.

"Mostly it's the women's fault," he continued. "The ladies began buying beer when it went on sale in supermarkets. They don't like anything to taste bitter, so we've had to reduce our use of hops. They want beer to be brilliantly clear, and you can't keep an all-malt beer from looking a little hazy, so we have to use less malt. We must please the women; the men drink whatever they can get. Anyhow, people don't taste beer; they drink it. They use it to wash the mustard from hot dogs out of their mouths."

Another explanation has to do with thirst. When a man is hot and dry, one bottle of flavorful, heavy-bodied beer may quench his thirst. But if the beer is thin and watery, he requires two bottles, sometimes three, before he is satisfied. In other words, the brewer who makes his beer thin sells more beer.

Americans returning from Europe complain that beer in this country lacks flavor. Seeking brews like those they enjoyed across the Atlantic, they begin buying imports.

Here often they again are disappointed. One reason is that a foreign beer shipped to the United States is not the same as that sold in the country of origin. A 6 per cent European beer is reduced to 4 or 5 per cent to meet some of our states' alcoholic content regulations. Moreover, it sometimes has been treated to make it last on its ocean voyage and during the long wait before it is purchased and consumed.

The trend toward blandness is fast spreading to other nations. Since 1950 most of Mexico's once flavorful beers have imitated those of the United States and now contain fewer hops and less malt than formerly. Canada, where beer once had to be made entirely from barley malt or else pay a special federal tax, changed its law in 1954; and now Canadian beers, too, are following the blandness trend. Japan is no exception. At a "blind" tasting of American and foreign beers held in my home one evening, a flavorful Japanese beer received the highest preference score in the tabulated ballots of my two dozen fellow tasters. A few weeks later I learned that the brewery in Tokyo had just "improved" its beer. The next time it was served to me it tasted like dishwater.

Even Bavaria, where for six hundred years the *Reinheitsgebot* has stated that only malt, hops, yeast, and water are proper materials for making beer, is reported considering a change.

A top executive of one of America's leading breweries said

to me: "Actually, the light beers are more difficult to make than the heavy, old-fashioned type. From the standpoint of requiring superior materials and know-how, they are vastly superior products. We could easily make our beer taste exactly like the expensive imports. We would do it if it would sell. Americans will accept a cloudy, bitter beer under a foreign label, but if we sold such a beer, they would refuse it. If our company were to change back to old-fashioned beer tomorrow, we'd be out of business within sixty days."

I asked him why American breweries do not offer several kinds of beer, as the brewers in Germany and Canada do, and give their customers a choice. "The costs in manufacturing, advertising, and distribution would be prohibitive," he replied. "The average large brewery already makes both a beer and an ale. Some also sell a dark draught beer, and a few still make bock. There just isn't enough space in store and bar refrigerators to hold an assortment of every brand. In this country a bakery's single bread and a brewer's single beer have to please everybody. Let the importers have the market for heavy beers. They have less than half of one per cent of the national market, and I say they're welcome to it."

Are there any old-fashioned American beers left? Yes, there are a few. I have tasted two brands of full-bodied, all-malt draught beer that are sold in wide areas of the nation. Pennsylvania has two all-malt bottled beers; Milwaukee has another, and there may be a few more.

Besides, there still is near-beer, the only good product born of national prohibition. When on January 16, 1920, it became a crime to buy or sell for beverage use any drink containing more than ½ of 1 per cent of alcohol, a few breweries scattered across the country, rather than close their doors, continued making beer from which they removed the alcohol.

Their near-beer never achieved much popularity during the thirteen dry years, and everyone expected it to go out of existence with repeal. It did not.

Today near-beer, still made by half-a-dozen breweries and sold throughout the nation, is proof that at least some consumers like beer's flavor, not just its alcohol. You find it mainly in food stores, although it also has another, less innocent kind of distribution. Near-beer is the drink sold in "water holes," the all-night drinking spots in American cities where bars are required by law to close at certain hours. Only an experienced taster can distinguish it from real beer. I have demonstrated this by submitting it to beer drinkers in "blind" tastings; they liked it and never suspected that it was not the real thing. Actually, near-beer has a slight cereal taste, from the extra food substances it contains. Its nutritive value commends it to physicians and nutritionists, particularly for patients on low-sodium diets. (They are allowed real beer, too.)

Some millions of beer drinkers firmly believe that they can taste the difference between stronger and weaker beers. Only a professionally trained taster can. In the Yale experiment that measured beer's effect on tension, the "control" subjects drank near-beer, while the others drank the same thing spiked with pure alcohol. They could not distinguish the difference. The bartender who tells you he can taste more alcohol in one beer than another is merely mistaking higher flavor for greater strength.

The current revival of home-brewing is a reminder of prohibition, but homemade beer antedates commercial brewing by thousands of years. In the Middle Ages brewing was a branch of domestic science practiced by every housewife. The word "brewster," according to Webster, originally meant a female brewer. Your children's Mother Goose rhymes tell of the little hen who "baked me my bread, she brewed me my ale, she sat by the fire and told many a fine tale." In seventeenth-century England friends presented the bride-to-be with brewing supplies with which to make "bride ale" for her wedding feast; from this custom we get the word "bridal." English ladies also brewed "groaning beer," to be drunk by women in labor. George Washington brewed his own beer at Mount Vernon, with Martha overseeing the process. His personal home-brew recipe, in his own handwriting, is in the rare manuscript section of the New York Public Library.

Today's new crop of do-it-yourself *braumeisters* may be partly motivated by the rising cost of commercial beer, but those of my acquaintance insist they are only rebelling against the thin, bland beer now on the market. Occasionally their product explodes and smells up their basements, but this does not deter them; they stubbornly start work on the next batch.

What the home-brewers do not seem to know is that they are violating a federal law. Actually, home-brewing had been of questionable legality during all of the twenty-five years following repeal. But now, by action of the Congress in 1959, anyone who makes beer at home, even if he follows George Washington's recipe, is specifically subject to fine and imprisonment.

However, there is no law against selling 6-, 10-, or 12-gallon crocks, siphon hose, beer testers, bottle fillers, thermometers, hydrometers, crown caps, capping machines, hop-flavored malt syrup, dried hops, corn sugar, yeast, or gelatine to settle the sediment, or against obtaining recipes from the thousands of stores that are doing this again-booming business.

Perhaps, if enough people learn that beermaking is now illegal, its popularity will grow even further. On the other hand, since the law still allows a householder to make two hundred gallons of tax-free wine at home (upon signing a form at the nearest Internal Revenue office), and also allows you to make hard cider, defenders of personal liberty ought to see their congressmen about this discrimination against lovers of beer. Incidentally, home-brewing is entirely legal (if you get a permit) in Canada.

The brewing industry, understandably, does not approve of home-brew, but I have tasted several samples that my neighbors have made, and except for the sediment in the bottles, have found them quite drinkable. Another batch, brewed by a veteran of the prohibition era, was so good that I secretly included it in one of my "blind" beer tastings. It outscored four nationally popular beers and ales!

Lovers of home-brew readily overlook its many defects, its off flavors, and the variation between batches. They enjoy it when it is flat and when it is excessively gassy, when it is clear and when it is cloudy. But they would never tolerate the same faults in any commercial beer.

To eliminate all of the defects to which such natural products as beer are subject, and to produce unchanging quality never achieved by the beers of old, modern brewing has become an exact science as well as a fine art. The days of corpulent brewmasters, with their handlebar mustaches and secret recipes, are gone forever. Today's master brewers are trained in food chemistry, microbiology, physics, thermodynamics, and engineering at such institutions as the United States Brewers Academy at Mount Vernon, New York, and the Siebel Institute of Technology at Chicago; and the University of California has inaugurated the first four-year course in brewing to be taught in an American college. Modern breweries are shiny processing plants like dairies, equipped with steel and glass-lined tanks. They abandoned unsanitary wooden tanks long ago, and the pitch-lined wooden kegs in which draught beer formerly was delivered to taverns are also being replaced by stainless steel and aluminum containers.

Brewing technologists tell you frankly to disregard such beer advertising slogans as those that boast of a brewery's water, its smaller bubbles, or its special processes. All breweries treat their water to adjust its mineral content, they say; if you made beer with pure distilled water, the drink would be insipid. And any brewer can adjust the size of the bubbles in his beer at will, simply by using the protein derivatives called foam aids.

Bubbles, these experts tell you, have much to do with your enjoyment of beer. It should have a head of creamy foam at least an inch high, they say. The froth should tickle your lips and should last until all of the beer is gone, and as the liquid recedes, intricate lacy patterns of foam should adhere to the glass.

Besides, the beer's hoppy fragrance is concentrated in its foam, which means that a good head gives the drink extra aroma.

Today's bland beer has less foam than the full-bodied, hoppy brews of old. The modern kind has more bubbles, because it is more highly carbonated, but because the beer lacks body, its bubbles quickly escape.

Exactly what is the foam on top of a glass of beer? Brewmasters say it consists of vast numbers of carbon-dioxide bubbles, each imprisoned in a viscous skin of proteins, sugar, and hop resins. The latter component, they explain, is the reason the foam tastes more bitter than the beer.

"Without foam," says Henry R. Henius, the veteran master

brewer whose father founded the Wahl-Henius Institute of Brewing in Chicago in 1886, "you lose the eye pleasure and part of the nose pleasure of your beer."

How to keep a creamy head on beer nowadays is really quite a problem. Besides being thin, the beer is served too cold. Excessive chilling, in addition to hiding the flavor, reduces the amount of foam. In Milwaukee, where more beer is drunk than anywhere else in the nation, it is served at least ten degrees warmer than in the Coca-Cola-consuming states in the deep South. In England, lovers of ale prefer it at about room temperature, which means it is almost warm. Expert opinion in this country favors not less than 40 degrees (the average on the bottom shelf of your refrigerator) as the serving temperature for light American beers, 48 to 55 degrees for full-bodied imports and ales. If you chill canned beer in your freezer, twenty minutes is sufficient; for bottled beer, thirty minutes.

Be sure to use only a scrupulously clean glass, preferably one that is used for nothing else but beer, never one that has contained milk. This is because fat of any kind breaks up the bubbles; you actually see them disappear as they strike the greasy surface. Rinse the glass with cold water before you use it. Never wash it with soap. Instead, use the kind of free-rinsing detergents that are recommended for dishwashing machines, and do not wipe the glass; let it dry.

Sterilizing a glass does not remove the fatty scum. More than half of the bars in the United States are serving flat beer, simply because their glasses are greasy. Their patrons would do the proprietors and themselves a favor by protesting this mistreatment of sound beer. If that lacy pattern of foam does not adhere to the glass, you know that something is wrong and needs to be remedied.

One way to clean a glass in a hurry is to rub it with bicarbonate of soda or salt.

But don't put salt in your beer. This is something millions of Americans have been doing for years, usually without knowing why. Many of them, even including some bartenders, think it gives beer a head, when it does just the opposite. What happens, some brewers say, is that the salt granules physically break up the bubbles and make the beer go flat. Salt does not make beer taste salty, either; if anything, the reaction in your mouth may be one of sweetness. Brewmasters say emphatically that this added salt does not improve beer flavor; it does not belong in your beer.

Another way to keep beer frothy is to drink it from a stein, the earthenware mug whose hinged lid is intended for that purpose. But both the stein and the traditional pewter beer mug, prized because its metal feels cool on your lips, interfere with the eye appeal beer has when it is served in a clear glass.

As to beer-glass shapes expert opinion differs, but there seems to be majority agreement on selecting glasses of medium size. This is because beer is most pleasing when quaffed—drunk deeply—not when sipped, the way you drink wine. By pouring only as much beer as you are going to drink immediately, you keep it from losing its effervescence.

Despite all of the good reasons to keep a collar on your brew, many buyers of draught beer (and this is especially true in England) insist on having it served flat. They simply want to get their full value in liquid; they do not want to pay for foam. (If you really object to foam on your beer, pour it on the side of your tilted glass.)

Draught beer is credited with virtues it does not really possess. You often hear people say it is the only kind they like. They would be surprised to learn that between draught beer and bottled or canned beer of the same brand the only detectible difference is that beer sold on draught is less highly carbonated. There is another difference: bottled and canned beers are pasteurized, while draught beer is not, but this cannot be detected by taste. The real reason some prefer beer on draught, aside from the fact that it is a cheaper drink in taverns, is that because it has less carbonation, they can drink more of it without feeling bloated. Yet, if the beer from a bottle or can is allowed to stand in a glass and lose its bubbles, it tastes the same as beer drawn from a keg.

In some taverns, however, tap beer does have a distinctive taste—an unpleasant taste. This happens when the proprietor fails to keep his tap equipment clean, or when he allows the kegs to become warm and spoil. If you are ever served an unclean-tasting draught beer, or if it has a chemical flavor, change to another bar.

How about cans versus bottles? I used to think, as many people do, that beer poured from a can has a metallic taste. But in "blind" tests over a period of years, I have failed repeatedly to distinguish canned from bottled beer of the same brand. In newly filled containers there is no difference. Each kind has obvious merits, and each has a fault. Sunlight spoils beer, gives it an unpleasant flavor that brewers call "skunky," and destroys its vitamin content. Bottled beer therefore needs always to be stored in the dark, even though most of it comes in dark glass. Cans, on the other hand, protect their contents from light, but sometimes beer, when stored for a period of months in a defective can, reacts with the metal of the container.

When opening a bottle, don't jar it; remove the cap swiftly to prevent the beer from gushing. To open a can, first make certain that the top is clean, because beer, while being poured, touches the surface. Then make a small puncture, to let some of the gas escape, before making a larger hole.

Beer is delicate and perishable. When you take it out of the refrigerator, allow it to become warm, and then chill it again, you may find it has lost some of its quality. Beer should be stored in a cool place (never in direct sunshine) and should not be kept too long. Age in beer is counted in weeks, not months or years; it tastes best when fresh, at the moment it leaves the brewery. Never keep any of it longer than three or four months. If the beer you buy is stale when you get it, take it back to the store, which probably has failed to rotate its stock. A date on a beer container does not mean it is good because it is aged. Instead, it means it is good because it is fresh.

The differences among American beers are shrinking, partly because of the blandness trend, and also because the number of breweries has shrunk from more than 2,400 in 1900 to fewer than 250 in 1960. In most states the average consumer finds that nearly all the brands of lager beer in his market taste to him the same. Wide flavor variations still exist, however, among the brands of ale.

Beer drinkers who travel do find different beer flavors in certain localities. Even a single brand is likely to vary slightly in taste when you buy it in widely separate parts of the country. Some of the largest companies now operate two or more breweries in different states, which enables them to cater to regional taste preferences. Especially, their beers have to meet the varying alcohol standards set by the individual states.

At this writing not more than a dozen American lager beers have really distinctive flavors.

There are bargains in beer, not always in the unknown

brands, which may be made of cheap materials, but in the size of container you buy. Look for the net contents on bottles and cans to see what you are getting; an 11-ounce container may look as large as one with 12 ounces. Large cans are not necessarily the best buys, because they cannot be recapped as bottles can. The most economical purchase of packaged beer is the quart bottle, returnable for your deposit, and bought by the case. For a short drink in taverns, there is economy in the 7- and 8-ounce bottles called "shorties."

For an organization picnic or a full-fledged beer bust, you can buy draught beer by the keg. Many American cities have beer depots, open every day in the week, that will deliver to your home an eighth-barrel "pony" (a keg containing almost four gallons of brew), along with the necessary tapping equipment. For a larger party, you may want a quarter-barrel or even a half-barrel. (Remember, unless you want a beer shower, to keep these containers cold, and learn how to tap them.)

This chapter thus far has been devoted to lager beers, ales, and "malt liquors." Now, to describe the specialties, we begin with the historic steam beer of San Francisco. Its name, more than its flavor, accounts for its fame. In June, 1959, the last of the city's steam beer brewers, Joseph Allen, closed his century-old Anchor Brewery, explaining that he was tired. But so many besieged him with orders (his steam beer was sold only on draught) that a new proprietor soon bought Allen's equipment and resumed production during 1960. What is this famous brew? It is simply old-fashioned beer, made entirely of malt and hops, and instead of being carbonated, as the majority of beers are, is *krausened,* which means that new, still-fermenting beer is added to make it effervescent. It has nothing to do with steam, having been named, a legend says, for its originator, who built a brewery during the gold rush of the 1850's—a Mr. Pat Steam.

Dark beer is brown, sweet-bitter, with a burnt-malt taste. It is called Münchener, or Bavarian, or simply dark beer. American brewers who make it usually sell it only in kegs to taverns, although in such beer-drinking centers as Milwaukee there are bottled dark beers as well. Most of the bottled dark beers sold in this country come from Munich, where the type may have originated.

Separate in name from other dark beer, but not greatly different in taste, is bock, the springtime beer, symbolized by the billygoat's head and supposedly named for the goat (*bok* in Hindustani), the ancient god of harvests. Some, however, say it was named for the town of Einbecker in Germany. In the days before refrigeration, beer was best brewed in winter and was ready in spring. Bock traditionally is sold for six weeks in spring, usually about May, but most modern brewers, who could make it in any season, have discontinued its production as involving too much bother. In early days bock was slightly stronger than lager and had a creamy foam so rich that a pencil would stand up in a glass of the brew.

Stock ale is an extra-strong, aged ale, sold in a few cities where there are enough ale connoisseurs to appreciate it.

Stout, a British creation, is the name for many brews. Originally it meant what its name implies, that it was a strong ale. It still usually means a very heavy, dark ale, rich in roasted malt flavor and with plenty of hoppy bitterness. Some of the imports are almost black, intended to be drunk "arf and arf" with pale ale, lager beer, or milk. A famous foreign brand, when tested in this country recently, was found to contain 7.6 per cent alcohol and 7.6 per cent solids. But another imported stout that was analyzed at the same time had only 3.7 per cent alcohol and 5.8 per cent solids, while an American stout showed 7.1 per cent alcohol and 1.4 per cent solids. It would appear from this that stout is likely to be strong, but can mean almost anything.

Porter, another English specialty, is brown, rich, with a burnt-cereal taste, and is less bitter than some of the imported stouts. Originally a mixture of ale and stout, it was named for the porters of England, who credited their legendary strength to their favorite drink.

There is no end to the assortment of beers in other countries. They range from *samshu,* the wheat beer of China, to the banana beer of Uganda in East Africa. The United States occasionally sees a new flavor, too. The latest I have heard of is a cola-flavored beer produced in the Midwest. In Europe flavored beers and mixed drinks made with beer are popular. A famous summer drink in Berlin is *Weisse mit Schuss,* a special light, tart beer mixed with raspberry juice. Stout mixed half and half with champagne makes Britain's famous Black Velvet, and Shandygaff is ale and ginger ale.

Historically, beers all over the world have been flavored with herbs and fruits of all kinds. Some of the earliest brews were sweet, and only in modern times have beers been effervescent. Europe's use of hops to make beer bitter only began in the eighth century, and the English at one time prohibited their use. Hops also help preserve beer from spoiling, which may be one of the reasons why their use has continued. Perhaps added flavoring is the answer to the flavorless beers of today.

Sake, named for the city of Osaka, is the Japanese rice brew that is served hot, according to tradition, in the sukiyaki restaurants in this country. It is classed by the United States Government as "wine" for labeling purposes but is technically a beer, and despite its usual 16 per cent alcohol content is taxed at the same $9.00 per barrel rate as the lightest beers.

Mead, another specialty, is classed by most writers with beer because the honey from which it is made is usually brewed with spices and herbs. Some writers believe mead was the first alcoholic drink known to man, that it antedated both wine and beer. The kind now sold in this country comes from Denmark and contains 19 per cent alcohol.

Finally, there is Mexico's pulque, fermented from the sap of the maguey cactus, and described here only because its 6 per cent alcoholic content resembles that of beer. If you have ever visited a *pulquería* in that country and sampled pulque's spoiled-buttermilk flavor, you know why nobody makes it in this country. Drunk by the Mexicans since the time of the ancient Toltecs and Aztecs, it is said to have great nutritious value. Tequila and mezcal, the national strong drinks, are distilled from fermented cactus saps resembling pulque.

It is worth noting that the pattern of beer drinking in the United States has undergone a great change. Before prohibition, three fourths of American beer left the breweries in barrels, to be consumed mainly in taverns. Giant beer wagons drawn by mighty horses were a familiar sight on city streets. My grandfather bought his beer in a covered pail from the corner saloon, a custom referred to as "rushing the growler." Then came the returnable bottle, first closed with the "lightning" porcelain stopper, which was succeeded after the turn of the century by the crown cap. In 1935, for the first time in history, beer was sold in cans, enamel-coated inside to protect the liquid from the metal. The convenience of packaged beer (bottles still lead cans in total use) has changed the nation's beer-drinking habits. By 1958, nearly 60 per cent of all beer was being consumed in America's homes.

CHAPTER 10

The Wisdom of Wine

ASK AN ITALIAN "DO YOU DRINK?" AND HIS ANSWER IS LIKELY TO be "No," although he may be drinking wine every day in the year. Call his attention to this, and he patiently explains that having wine with one's meals is not "drinking," because, he tells you, wine is merely a liquid food.

This simple, matter-of-fact view is in striking contrast to the average American's concept of wine as a beverage so complex that it cannot be served properly without matching each type to specific foods, and without expert guidance in an elaborate serving ritual that the Italian never heard of. These impressions are based on frilly, ostentatious fashion.

To make common sense out of wine it is necessary to shunt aside an enormous amount of connoisseur lore with which it is surrounded, and to remember that, after all, it is something to drink.

Essentially wine, with all of its ancient history and sacred symbolism, is fermented grape juice. It comes in thirty-three principal flavors, and is either white (straw-colored, actually), pink, amber, or red. It has thousands of different names, many of which apply to more than one kind of wine—a fact that helps explain why so many books are written in vain efforts to explain them. In alcoholic content, most wines in the United States are either between 10 and 14 per cent (the group arbitrarily called table wines) or between 16 and 20 per cent (appetizer and dessert wines, the types to which brandy has been added). Champagne, when you pour it from its elegant bottle, turns out to be nothing more than a white table wine with bubbles.

Of all fruits, the grape is the most versatile. It makes the most delicious of all beverages—so delicious that the best-tasting whiskeys, rums, and brandies are those to which wines have been added.

Other fruits and vegetables besides grapes make wine, too, but always tell you so on their labels: apple wine, blackberry wine, currant wine, and so on. Dandelion wine, parsnip wine, rhubarb wine, celery wine, and such are usually homemade concoctions. The English used to call one kind rape wine, which did not mean what you think. It was merely grape wine made from the leftover pulp of the fruit after the last-pressed wine had been drawn off—what the French call their *piquette.*

Any attempt to describe the vast assortment of the world's vintages would fill this entire chapter and require another volume or two besides. Instead, a condensed flavor description of each of the principal kinds of wine available in America is given in the Appendix.

There is a great deal of interest in wine nowadays. One reason is that more Americans are traveling than ever before, visiting the vineyard regions of Europe, California, New York, and Ohio, where they are exposed to wines. Interest in epicurean foods, flavorful cookery, and formal entertaining with wine is growing.

Gourmet organizations are sprouting throughout the nation. The international Wine and Food Society alone has thirty chapters in ten states, spreading wine knowledge as their members become wine hobbyists and connoisseurs. These people speak of wine as the Duke of Windsor did when he was England's King Edward VIII: "Not only do you drink wine," he said, "but you breathe it—you look at it—you taste it—you sip it—and then you speak about it." In San Francisco this reverent approach to a mere beverage reached its zenith in 1960 when the University of California Extension announced a course in "Wine Appreciation," to consist of fifteen classes teaching wine judging, proper serving temperatures, proper glassware, and proper foods to serve with wines.

It is the connoisseurs who keep alive the frilly ritual of wine service, making dinners with wine an elaborate ceremony, writing articles about food and wine that appear in newspapers and national magazines. Their total number is not large, but they get considerable publicity. On matters of food and drink they are the most influential people in the nation, the leading tastemakers of America.

As a result of all this, other Americans are asking questions about wine. For example, they want to know how European and American wines compare in quality. The answer to this is that while each country and each viticultural district has its own regional nectars that are not duplicated anywhere, American wines, on the whole, average higher in quality than the imports. In several dozen "blind" comparative tastings held throughout the nation by California winegrowers, in which editors, home economists, importers, film personalities, wine merchants, gourmets, and restaurateurs were the tasters, California wines outscored imports in five out of six categories.

This brought well-modulated screams of indignation from the French Government, which brought pressure through our Department of State to prohibit the California vintners from advertising that their wines had outscored those of France. But this did not muzzle the American press, which merrily published the scores in complete detail.

Incidentally, the prices of the imported wines that were

tasted averaged more than double those of their California counterparts. But as one of my vintner friends once observed, wines, liquors, and other things regarded as luxuries are clothed in dignity to the extent that they are clothed in price.

Not all foreign wines are expensive. Many are much cheaper than the costlier American brands. Part of the lure of the word "imported" is that it suggests the wine is expensive.

American snobs still insist that the only fine wines in the world come from Europe. This is because wine snobs drink the labels instead of the wines. Their favorite target is American wine labeling, which identifies the principal types as burgundy, sauterne, sherry, port, and champagne. It makes erudite-sounding conversation to point out that Burgundy and Champagne are vineyard districts in France, that Sauternes (spelled with a final "s") is a village in the Bordeaux district, that the original port came from Portugal, and that sherry is an English mispronunciation of Jerez in Spain. "American wines would not be bad," the snobs say, "if only they would adopt their own names and stop imitating the genuine wines of Europe."

It never occurs to them that the Old World wine names have been anchored in the English language for many generations and that there are no other words to describe these types of wine. If their contention were to prevail in other fields, Russian rye bread would have to come only from Russia; French and Danish pastries would come only from France and Denmark; Swiss cheese only from Switzerland; and china from behind the Bamboo Curtain.

This semantical nonsense has impelled American vintners, in order to sell their higher-priced wines, to adopt a kind of labeling that confuses neophyte buyers. It is called "varietal" labeling: the wine is named for the grape variety from which it predominantly is made. Sauterne becomes Semillon or Sauvignon Blanc, sherry becomes Palomino, burgundy becomes Gamay or Pinot Noir—the list is constantly growing.

While the Pinot Noir grape, for example, makes excellent burgundy, this label causes some Americans to imagine that the wine is made from peanuts. Few store clerks can master tongue-twisting Sauvignon Blanc, either, and Palomino suggests horses more readily than it does sherry. Moreover, makers of American ports and champagnes have failed completely thus far to come up with any "varietal" names, because these two wines are blends of many different grape varieties.

Meanwhile, the magic word "imported" continues to lend glamour to port from Portugal, where the grapes for this wine are crushed by peasants' bare feet, and to sherry that comes from Spain, where the *pisadores* also dance on the grapes (although in Spain they wear shoes). And one of the costliest foreign sparkling wines, sold in leading restaurants from coast to coast, has the word "carbonated" on its label—a word that would kill the sale of any wine made in America.

Among the mysteries of wine labeling, no one thing is as baffling as "dry." Dictionaries say that, applied to beverages, this word means they are unsweetened—the opposite of "sweet." But millions of wine drinkers (and, more recently, consumers of soft drinks and also of beers) consider it a mark of discriminating taste to insist that their beverages be "dry." They imagine that dryness somehow signifies fine quality. Vintners, however, know that most people like drinks that taste sweet. So they simply make their wines sweet, but label them "dry."

This also applies to *sec,* the French word for "dry." Nowadays virtually all wines labeled "dry" or *sec* are actually sweet; "extra-dry" wines are usually slightly sweet, and even champagne *brut* (French for "rough," "raw," or "unadulterated") also is gradually becoming sweeter.

Consumers who really want dry wines now look for "bone-dry" sherries and "nature" champagnes. "Sweet" in any language somehow seems to be a naughty word, perhaps because of the spreading concern over calories. Consequently, an extra-sweet champagne, in order to sell to Americans, has to be labeled—of all things—*demi-sec* or "semi-dry."

The "dry" Martini cocktail, which means only that the once-mandatory ingredient—vermouth—is now administered with an atomizer, has completed the rape of "dry." Another thing it has done is to take the flavor out of dry (French-type) vermouths. Time was when all such vermouths were amber-colored and had the pronounced taste of the herbs with which they are flavored. But as more and more Americans succumbed to the "dry" Martini fad, tavernkeepers' profits began to fade, because they were compelled to dispense larger quantities of expensive gin, cutting down on their use of the less costly component, vermouth.

Finally an American vermouth maker had a brilliant idea. He made his vermouth almost water white and removed most of its herb flavor, so that the bar patron could not detect that his gin was being diluted. Other producers, both in this country and in Europe, promptly followed. They now make their "dry" vermouths as white and bland as the United States Government allows for wines that call themselves vermouth. Some even advertise the fact. One Italian producer's ad assures readers of *The New Yorker* that his dry vermouth is "clear in color, clean in taste . . . all the 'vermouthy' aroma and flavor have been screened out."

Among questions most often asked by puzzled American consumers are those about wine's age. How old must wine be to be good? Why do some bottles say "Vintage 1955" or some other bygone year, while others coyly refrain from telling their age? The fact is that most of the world's wines are best when they are young and lose quality with the years instead of improving. An extreme example is rosé, which reaches its peak of drinking quality about six months after the vintage and soon thereafter loses its fresh flavor and aroma.

Only the *exceptional* wines gain anything with long storage; this is the main thing that makes them exceptional. A few famous clarets, some of the burgundies, and some of the sherries, ports, tokays, and madeiras, are examples of wines that develop extra flavor, bouquet, and smoothness with extra years, especially after they are bottled. (Wines are the only beverages that continue improving in bottles.) But these types, too, have limited life spans—different for each lot and even for each bottle. Table wines, in particular, when kept too long become undrinkable.

As for the vintage labels you see on some bottles, these have two quite different kinds of significance. On the costliest French and German wines, vintage dates distinguish the good grape harvest years from the bad. This is necessary because the European vineyards have only occasional years with enough sunshine to bring their grapes to full maturity. The connoisseur tries to learn which are the good years simply to avoid buying the bad ones.

But in California, the source of most American wines, the normally long, rainless summers permit the grapes to mature fully in almost all years. A vintage label on a California wine, therefore, is used mainly to distinguish one batch of a given wine from another.

Some of the finest wines are undated, because a government regulation says a vintage date cannot be used when wines of two or more years are blended together. Since wines—like coffees, teas, the grains in whiskey distillers' mashes, and the cloth in the clothes we wear—are usually best when blended, vintage dates on American wines are a comparative rarity.

Wines lose quality not only with age, but also when improperly stored. Table wines are the most perishable, and when their bottles once are opened, begin to spoil within a few days. But all the types suffer when exposed to extreme cold, heat, or even direct sunlight. The last factor explains why most wines are protected by dark bottles. Even wine that is chilled and allowed to warm again loses some of its delicate quality. In particular, the experienced wine shopper never buys a bottle whose label has grown yellow and frayed from overlong storage in the store.

Because wines are fermented from grapes, and grapes vary in flavor with changes in the weather, most vintners' wines vary from season to season. Brewers and distillers manage to keep their products fairly uniform from bottle to bottle, but even the largest wineries, with their vast blending stocks, find this difficult to manage. The wine connoisseur knows this, and when he finds a wine he especially likes, he buys as many bottles as he can use within a reasonable time.

The connoisseur also hunts for wine bargains, because he knows that there is no direct, inevitable relationship between a wine's price and its drinking quality. Of course, an estate-bottled vintage wine that costs a great deal to produce is always priced accordingly. But sometimes the best-tasting wine in the store is the moderately priced jug on the bottom shelf or behind the counter.

Some entirely new kinds of wine have been appearing lately. Millions of people are drinking them, but the older wine books contain no clues to their character. Actually, they represent a mid-twentieth-century wine-flavor revolution.

Beginning in 1955, when the government first authorized "special natural wines" to contain natural pure flavors, a flood of new products appeared on the American market with exotic coined names resembling nothing in the universe of wine—ranging from birds and animals to textiles and even autos. In a few years it was obvious that their acceptance was permanent.

Some of the flavors resemble lemon, orange, lime, chocolate, ginger, and cherry, with additional subtle tastes imparted by various herbs. Others remind people of cola (which recalls that Coca-Cola originally, back in 1885, was a flavored wine; it was called French Wine Coca).

What most of these products have in common is the word apéritif on their labels, and this is their explanation. They belong to the same class as the vermouths, which are also apéritifs (flavored wines), along with byrrh, St. Raphael, Dubonnet, and the other apéritif wines of Europe. Most are 20 per cent in alcoholic content, and all of them are sweet. They represent the vintners' quest for new wine flavors to court the American taste that favors catsup-smothered steak, fried potatoes, and pie.

In 1960 came something else: table wines with bubbles. Consumers, accustomed to the idea that only champagne and sparkling burgundy had any fizz, opened bottles of these new wines and found them faintly sparkling. The government again had changed the law in the preceding year, this time to allow wines to contain added carbon-dioxide gas (as long as the pressure did not exceed five pounds per square inch) without paying the exorbitant tax collected on champagne. The only catch is that vintners are legally prohibited from advertising the bubbles. Your palate can tell you but the wine's label must not.

What really started the wine-flavor revolution was kosher wine, originally introduced some twenty years earlier. It was intended first for sacramental use by Jewish consumers, but to the amazement of old-time vintners, it became nationally popular among non-Jews. With its foxy flavor of Concord grapes, heavily sweetened with sugar, kosher wine reminds Americans of what they regard as "real" grape flavor—the familiar taste of sweet Concord grape jellies and grape juices. European and California wines have none of this taste; their flavors are more winy than grapy. They are the traditional Old World types, and the table wines are mainly dry. As with strong cheeses, caviar, and green olives, they do not always appeal at first taste, but with training, people get to like them.

The kosher wine success started the California vintners thinking. Their revolutionary new types are the result.

Even now, however, they are forgetting the prediction made in 1934 by the late Captain Paul Garrett, that wine use in the United States would never achieve its real potential until wineries learned to blend the true European wine grape varieties, grown in California's equable climate, with the foxy Concord and other native grapes of the East and Midwest. Such a blend, Captain Garrett always contended, would give Americans a flavor of universal appeal. Taste, he believed, eventually would make wine the leading national beverage.

Despite its relatively slow progress (distilled-spirits consumption is one third greater, beer is sixteen times as great), wine use shows signs of future growth. In 1959 it was almost nine tenths of a gallon per capita, double the rate twenty-four years earlier. This has something to do with the maturing of America. People are living longer, and here is a key statistic:

at least two thirds of all wine consumers in the United States are between the ages of thirty-five and fifty. Wine appeals most to mature people, who seek the more deliberate pleasures and relaxation.

Here wine's role as a tranquilizer, for the relief of emotional tension, looms as an underlying reason for its use throughout the centuries, the same basic motive that accounts for the use of beer. Of all the alcoholic beverages, wine is the most gently relaxing.

Compared to distilled spirits, which give a quick lift and a quick letdown, the effects of wine, like those of beer, are felt gradually and last considerably longer. The organic acids, esters, and nitrogen-bearing compounds of both of these fermented beverages slow down the rate at which their alcohol enters the blood stream. Blood-alcohol levels reach a plateau instead of a peak; their alcohol circulates at low levels through the body, lulling the jumpy nerve centers. In other words, wine and beer are not the drinks to take for a "kick"; that effect is delivered fastest and hardest by gin or vodka.

This was demonstrated first with beer in the Yale experiments. Later tests, using the same skin-conductance measurements of tension and stress, were conducted with wine.

Researchers administered doses of 12 per cent red table wine and 12 per cent alcohol-and-water solutions to a group of human subjects. Those who participated got little pleasure, however, because—in order to eliminate any effects from the differences in taste of the two liquids—the doses were given by stomach tube.

The alcohol equivalent of a single highball gave slightly more relaxation than three glasses of wine. But more than one highball's dose of alcohol increased the subjects' tension, while more wine continued to give relief. Twelve ounces of wine reduced basal tension by approximately 35 per cent, stress response by 55 per cent.

There were no tests to compare wine directly with beer. But since in the earlier experiments it took two 12-ounce bottles of beer, with its much lower alcoholic strength, to deliver about the same relaxing effects on tension and stress (see the beer chapter) that were obtained from one 12-ounce dose of table wine, the title of champion relaxing drink obviously goes to the wine.

This leaves still unanswered the different effects to be expected from the many different kinds of wine. The 12 per cent table wine tested was the dry red type known as burgundy or claret. It is a light wine, without the added brandy that is in port, sherry, and the apéritifs. An old English saying was that "claret is for boys, port for men, brandy for heroes." Port, with its usual 20 per cent alcoholic content, should be even more relaxing than—glass for glass—the claret.

Wine, among all the alcoholic beverages, is also the one credited with the most impressive dietary and therapeutic values, many of them known since ancient times. The Bible contains no less than one hundred and sixty-five references to wine, including the often-quoted admonition by Paul to Timothy, to "use a little wine for thy stomach's sake and thine often infirmities. . . ." Today a comprehensive bibliography of medical research aids doctors in selecting wines in the specialties of nutrition, gastroenterology, cardiology, urology, neurology, and psychiatry. Dr. Salvatore P. Lucia's textbook, *Wine as Food and Medicine,* is widely read by the medical profession.

None of this, however, answers the personal questions many Americans continue asking about wines in relation to themselves. Oftenest heard, it seems, is "Why does wine always make me sleepy?" The answer may be its tranquilizing effect, now scientifically demonstrated. On the other hand, tranquillity and drowsiness are not always related; some people, when freed of worries, are more wide-awake than ever. Besides, many other people say beer makes them sleepy, while still others say the same of whiskey or brandy.

Another common query is less difficult to answer: "Why is it that when I have a couple of cocktails before dinner and then take a bottle of wine with my meal, I find I've had too much to drink?" It is simply a matter of total alcohol dosage; one less cocktail or half as much wine would solve this problem readily.

Still another question often raised concerns the drunkards who populate the skid rows of some American cities, the miserable human specimens called "winos." A team of researchers in 1958 studied 531 of these addictive drinkers and learned why wine is their principal beverage. Six out of seven said they prefer distilled spirits to wine, and that they drink wine only because it is cheaper. Most had become addictive drinkers long before they began drinking wine.

Then there is the case of wine-drinking France, where Pierre Mendès-France, the milk-drinking former premier, launched a campaign to reduce wine use because his country had developed a grave alcoholic problem. This was in sharp contrast to the observations of Thomas Jefferson and Benjamin Franklin, one hundred and fifty years earlier, that the French were a temperate people because they always drank wine with their meals. The advocates of wine in other countries are now trying to learn the truth about France.

They have uncovered some interesting facts. One is that excessive drinking is most common in the provinces of Normandy and Brittany, where the least wine is grown and where the consumption of hard liquor is the highest. Another is that moonshine is legal in France. For more than a century French law has permitted the *bouilleurs de cru* (farmer-distillers), using portable stills that are carried from farm to farm, to make distilled spirits of their apples, grapes, and other crops, free of any taxes.

As long ago as 1895 C. W. Chancellor, the United States consul at Havre, reported that nearly a million of these "legalized moonshiners" were distilling not only their own crops, but also those of their neighbors, into a "pernicious distillate . . . of which many thousands of hectoliters are annually exported to the United States as 'pure French brandy.' "

"So long as wine was the cheapest drink to be had in France," the consul wrote, "it was the national and universal drink and the people were a sober people; but when the *bouilleurs de cru* substituted a pernicious brandy at a reduced price, the reputation of the nation for sobriety was changed, and drunkenness became the prevailing habit of the middle classes."

In 1959, sixty-four years later, nearly four million Frenchmen still abused the privilege of the *bouilleurs de cru.* Mendès-France had attempted in vain to restrict it. In 1959 President Charles de Gaulle was striving, against powerful political opposition, to abolish it entirely.

Another report from France relates excessive drinking to the national demoralization following World War II. Alcoholic mortalities rose 400 per cent between 1936 and 1954, but have been declining rapidly since, with a 28 per cent drop between 1956 and 1958.

Whatever may be the complete truth about the French problem, ordinary use of wine with meals apparently is not the cause.

In direct contrast to the stories from France is wine-drinking Italy, where the average citizen consumes a half-liter of wine with his meals daily for most of his life and seldom gets drunk. The wine he drinks is a dry, tart table wine. This, among all the common beverages of mankind, is the only one that is exclusively a mealtime beverage. It is made and used only for that single purpose. It represents most of the world's wine.

The rate of alcoholism in Italy is about one eighth that in the United States. Seeking the reasons for so vast a difference, an international team of researchers made an eight-year study of alcohol in Italian culture. They compared the diets of Italians in Italy with those of Italian families in the United States. They found second and third generations of Italian-American families gradually lessening their use of wine. And as they used wine more seldom, they became intoxicated oftener. The rate of alcoholism among Italians in America was found beginning to rise. The researchers now suggest that wine, used as a food with meals, may have a built-in preventive against addictive drinking.

Apparently Soviet Russia has the same idea. Premier Nikita Khrushchev in 1958 launched a campaign to turn that nation away from its traditional vodka and to teach Russians to drink wine instead. An objective of his seven-year plan for winegrowers was stated in press dispatches from Moscow: "A glass of wine on each workingman's table."

Will Americans ever adopt wine as their national drink?

The answer may depend on its flavor, on whether the vintners can supply wines to match the American taste. Or, on the other hand, a maturing nation, with its ever-increasing numbers of older people, conceivably may develop a preference for this beverage because it is allied with leisurely, deliberate living.

Or perhaps, in the long run, the connoisseurs, the gourmets, and the wine hobbyists—because they are the tastemakers of the nation—may be the ones who do most to popularize wine in America.

CHAPTER 11

Facts and Fables

PLINY THE ELDER, THE SAGE OF ANCIENT ROME, WROTE THAT *in vino veritas,* which translated from the Latin means "in wine there is truth." This only means, of course, that people under the influence of alcohol often blurt out their true feelings. Actually, truth is the rarest of all commodities in the field of drinks and drinking. Some of the countless fables widely accepted as fact are so flagrantly false and dangerous that to believe them is worse than remaining honestly ignorant.

The fantastic folklore of alcohol includes beliefs about various drinks' effects on efficiency, appetite, digestion, sleep, sex stimulation, progeny, snakebite, and bad breath, and gives both frightening and reassuring advice about alcohol's role in sickness. Some of it is true, some is partly true, and a good deal of it is utter hogwash. This book attempts to supply simple, sound answers to most of the questions millions of people are asking about alcoholic beverages. The next several pages will sift some of the facts from fiction concerning several subjects not covered in other chapters.

Some questions cannot be answered with certainty, because researchers' conclusions do not always agree; when such is the case, this text tells you so. True scientists and other people with common sense are those who frankly say: "I don't know." If there are things you wishfully prefer to believe, there probably are some published opinions and even scientific reports to support you, but there may be other reports that say you are all wrong. Even the newest scientific discoveries, announced with headlines today, may be contradicted by others a few months hence. Certain of the most widely held theories are still proved only by statistics, a method which Dr. Joseph Berkson of Mayo Clinic once compared to a bikini—"revealing what is interesting, concealing what is vital." Some beliefs are fostered by fanatical drys, others by people with something to sell, and still more are pure quackery and nonsense.

One trouble with the search for everyday drinking facts is that the thousands of researchers throughout the world now engaged in studying alcohol, whose number was swelled in 1958 by a $700,000 United States Government appropriation for work in fourteen medical centers in various states, are mainly seeking the causes and cure of addictive drinking and chronic alcoholism—not the facts moderate users of alcoholic beverages would like to have. Their quest, of course, is a vital one, and someday it may be successful.

Among the assorted fables, let us first dispose of the one that says alcohol in any form is a poison.

The fact is that diluted ethyl alcohol, in the doses contained in beers, wines, and liquors, is no more or less a poison than sugar, salt, vinegar, tobacco, aspirin, penicillin, or the natural secretions of your thyroid, pituitary, adrenal, and other glands in your body. Your food tastes flat without salt, but if you swallowed the entire contents of the shaker on your dinner table, you would be dead in a short time. The sailor who drinks sea water gets too much salt, goes mad, and dies. Yet your body needs this common substance, and animals travel long distances to get it. If you ate a whole cigar, or swallowed a hundred aspirins at once, or took sufficiently excessive doses of the chlorine that is added to your drinking water, or of the lifesaving antibiotics, or of the carbon monoxide you inhale in traffic, or of ordinary sunshine, the consequences would be fatal. It is not mere semantical quibbling to point out that the only substances properly called poisons, according to Webster, are those that injure or kill when taken in small amounts. You usually find the labels of such items suggestively decorated with the ominous skull and crossbones.

Pure (200 proof) alcohol is so instantly injurious (it coagulates protein tissues) that you cannot even bear to drink it. Highly concentrated alcohol is a disinfectant and a preservative; Lord Nelson's body, after the Battle of Trafalgar, was carried back to England on his flagship in a barrel of spirits. Neurosurgeons often inject it at full strength into facial nerves to destroy them and relieve severe neuralgia. Yet, sufficiently diluted, alcohol has been taken internally for thousands of years by most of the human race, which meanwhile has thrived and multiplied. Physicians have prescribed it in various forms for various illnesses for centuries, and, incidentally, at least four out of five doctors drink alcoholic beverages themselves.

Next we shall examine some of the popular folklore about the effects of ordinary drinking.

Homer, the Greek poet, recorded one ancient belief for posterity when he said: "Wine gives strength to weary men." Oliver Goldsmith, the English writer, testified to another when he wrote that "good liquor gives genius a better discerning." A dangerous popular notion was strengthened when a television program in London, carefully planned to demonstrate to millions of viewers that drinking slows down motorists' reactions, actually resulted in three drivers successfully traveling an intricate obstacle course seconds faster after drinking two whiskeys than before they had taken a drop.

Exact measurements of drinkers' muscular strength, conducted at Yale University in 1940, have suggested that Homer might have been partly right. A single glass of whiskey seemed to increase some men's muscle power for a short time, but three glasses produced the opposite result.

On the other hand, extensive tests of muscular co-ordination after drinking have been carried on in Germany, Norway, the United States, and most recently in Finland, all with similar results: when alcohol gets into the blood stream, coordination and judgment suffer. Typists who have had a drink type faster, but they make more errors. Sharpshooters feel more confident, but they hit fewer bull's-eyes. Drinkers feel less tired, but their energy is reduced. Their sense of hearing becomes keener, but they have trouble distinguishing between louder and softer sounds. They are increasingly sensitive to light, but are slower in distinguishing between red and green traffic signals. Less than two highballs reduce their net visual acuity as much as wearing sunglasses at night.

As for Goldsmith, Edgar Allan Poe, and assorted other writers, as well as painters, who are said to have done their best work while under the influence, psychologists concede that some neurotic, excessively self-critical, psychopathic geniuses may need to put their inhibitions to sleep before their ideas can flow freely. But extensive tests also show that people who have been drinking memorize words more slowly than when they are sober, and that the working of the human mind, under the depressant effect of alcohol, generally slows down.

For the bungled British driving test on television there is another explanation altogether. Anyone taking such a test, even to renew his driver's license, is usually self-conscious and anxious. The drivers in the televised test performed badly while they were tense and cold sober, and not so badly when whiskey reduced their anxiety.

The only thing you usually can do better after a number of drinks is go to sleep. Even this is not always the case, because different individuals' reactions to alcoholic beverages vary at different times. While many people find that a nightcap drunk at bedtime brings them refreshing slumber, others have complained that it is followed by disturbing dreams. Nobody as yet has succeeded in explaining these different reactions. The only advice to insomniacs on which all authorities seem to agree is to relax, to forget their worries if they can, and to beware of becoming addicted to the use of sleeping pills.

Vast numbers of people still regard alcohol as a stimulant. They sometimes see it actually stimulate, momentarily. They know that a tired person feels more alert and less fatigued when he takes a drink, and they observe people imbibing and becoming gay at a party. If they knew that drinking only *seems* to make fatigue disappear, by causing the drinker to stop noticing his tiny aches and pains, they might realize that alcohol is really a depressant. All they really need to remember, in order to be finally convinced, is that the person who drinks far too much passes out.

Even the well-known anesthetic, ether, which some members of the beatnik tribe sniff to make themselves intoxicated, excites them for a time before its depressant effect, which resembles that of alcohol, begins to be felt.

True stimulants, such as the drug caffeine contained in coffee, tea, and cola drinks, are the exact opposite of depressants. Caffeine stimulates nerve tissue, allays fatigue, and fights drowsiness. In fact, there have been experiments in which caffeine was added to whiskey in order to learn whether such a mixture might counter some of liquor's effects. The results should delight the promoters of Irish Coffee, for moderate doses of the caffeine-spiked whiskey kept the drinkers thoroughly awake, meanwhile losing none of the alcohol's tension-reducing, tranquilizing effect. Yale's Dr. Greenberg once was asked whether coffee can sober up a drunken person. He replied: "All that happens is that you have a wide-awake drunk on your hands, instead of a sleepy one."

Alcohol's use by the medical profession as a tranquilizer goes back to ancient times. Doctors now prescribe it mainly for the aged, who need it most to minimize the aches, chills, and regrets of advanced years. Perhaps the physicians assume that their other troubled patients have already tried it without professional urging. Many doctors are beginning to realize that alcohol is at least safer than the modern tranquilizer drugs, which often produce undesirable behavior, nerve damage, addiction, and dangerous, sometimes fatal, allergic reactions. When the Office of Civilian Defense in 1959 kept a husband and wife and their three children in an atomic fall-out shelter in a two-week test of reactions to such confinement, the couple were given tranquilizer pills for the children and a bottle of whiskey for themselves. People who build their own bomb shelters are being advised to use caffeine-free coffee, and some researchers even suggest (without proof) that having alcohol in your blood stream may prevent some of the damage from radiation if you are caught in a nuclear bomb attack.

A widely circulated kind of alcoholic folklore that is rarely discussed in mixed company concerns the supposed aphrodisiac quality of this or that specific drink. The sales of a certain apéritif once soared briefly in San Francisco when it was rumored to possess sex-stimulating power, and in Georgia a well-known whiskey brand fell flat on its face when a report that it robbed its consumers of their manly vigor was circulated by salesmen for a competing firm. The whiskey thus slandered was withdrawn from the state and has not reappeared in Georgia since.

Among the early recorded attempts to concoct love potions were the experiments of the medieval alchemists. It was for that purpose, as well as for medicinal use, that they created cordials and liqueurs, whose use today, however, has no such connotation. It is interesting, nevertheless, to note that virtually all of the standard ingredients used in modern formulas for liqueurs and vermouths are credited, in the extensive Arab, Hindu, and Chinese literature on aphrodisiacs, with the power to stimulate libidinous impulses. The oriental lists of purportedly aphrodisiac substances include all of the well-known spices, herbs, roots, and essential oils employed in various flavored alcoholic beverages, as well as a number of items commonly found in American kitchens: garlic, onions, mustard seed, artichokes, pepper, ginger, eggs, fish, mutton, mushrooms, and truffles. A few such recipes call for somewhat harder-to-get ingredients, such as opium, hashish, the mountain lizard called a skink, and the flesh of baby crocodiles. Early Irish literature contained a simpler recipe: saffron, once used to flavor most of that country's whiskey, was described as "the true and genuine rouser of the animal spirits."

If such a thing as a true love potion—something with the power to stimulate whichever area of the brain rules feelings of affection—has ever existed, it still is unknown to the science of pharmacology. Even yohimbine and cantharides, the two ancient, highly dangerous drugs that veterinarians still sometimes use to arouse languid stallions for breeding (drugs that are powerful local irritants of the pelvic organs of the male), are wholly deficient as emotional stimuli.

Alcohol, on the other hand, has been called "the handmaiden of Cupid" because by suppressing inhibitions, it causes some reluctant females to become somewhat less reluctant. Actually, it only liberates existing desires that are normally held in check, for as a popular saying goes, "some girls are cold sober, others are always cold." And alcohol does little more for the average male, usually prolonging erection and deferring climax at .10 to .15 blood alcohol level, but at higher levels robbing him of potency entirely. In fact, modern science, after extensive experimentation on animals and even some on humans, has concluded that Shakespeare wrote the final word on this subject more than three centuries ago in the porter's second-act speech in *Macbeth*. Speaking of liquor, the porter says to Macduff: "Lechery, sir, it provokes and unprovokes; it provokes the desire, but it takes away the performance: therefore much drink may be said to be an equivocator with lechery . . . [it] equivocates him in a sleep, and, giving him the lie, leaves him."

It often is said that men, because their body chemistry differs from that of women, can tolerate more drinks than the weaker sex can. But some barroom sages insist that exactly the reverse is true, reminding you that the majority of inebriates in all countries are males. No facts exist to support either belief, although in relation to body weight, at least, a husky man should have a greater alcohol capacity than a frail female half his size.

Should a woman drink during pregnancy? Among people who fear alcohol this question is charged with emotion, because when an expectant mother takes a drink, the alcohol circulating in her blood stream reaches her unborn child. A similar thing happens when she smokes; when she absorbs nicotine from tobacco, her child gets some, too. Some women, incidentally, find they feel more effect from a drink during pregnancy than at other times.

Most obstetricians agree that a cocktail, highball, or glass or two of wine is harmless for mother and infant. They remind their patients, however, that alcohol adds calories, and emphasize the need to maintain a balanced diet. Usually they point out, too, that because alcohol is a diuretic, drinking increases frequency of urination.

Doctors, when asked about drinking at this time, consider the expectant mother's frequent moods, her anxiety, and the strains of family life during the prenatal months. In cases that require sedation some physicians, rather than prescribe tranquilizers, whose effects are not always predictable, advise a single evening drink.

Especially they warn against excessive drinking during pregnancy. Women who are accustomed to having before-dinner cocktails usually are not told to give them up, but are advised to cut down. "A good rule for expectant mothers," one of my physician friends says, "is to drink half as much as before they became pregnant."

Much of the folklore of tippling concerns the ways the various kinds of drinks are supposed to affect the drinker. It helps explain why many an imbiber stays for a time with one kind of cocktail, highball, beer, or wine, even if he does not particularly like its flavor. He avoids others with which he associates some past uncomfortable experience. Over a period of time such a drinker switches from brand to brand and from mixture to mixture, each change usually triggered by a new painful episode or by some current bit of frightening or intriguing gossip. Most of this folklore is hokum, but at its base there are a few facts.

The key to the intoxicating effect of any drink is given in the third chapter, which states that the amount of alcohol circulating in your blood at any one time determines whether you will be gay, tipsy, or bleary. The alcoholic strengths of most of the different drinks have already been listed. It also has been explained that food in the stomach, and the food substances in beers and wines, slow the absorption of alcohol into the blood; that diluted drinks, such as highballs, deliver their effects more gradually and with lower peak effect than cocktails or shots do, and that the wallop from light-bodied spirits, such as gin, vodka, and the blends, is harder than that from heavier liquors of identical alcoholic strength.

The importance of the time factor in influencing the effect of a given drink has not yet been emphasized sufficiently. How fast the kick follows the swallow often determines how many drinks an individual will take at a sitting. This, and also the length of time the drink's peak effect lasts, influences his mood and his behavior. People are gayest while their blood-alcohol level is rising, especially while it is rising fast. Many a host has noted that his cocktail party begins going flat as soon as his guests' drinks start wearing off. The foregoing observation about drinking moods applies only to infrequent drinkers. It may be the reason why people hopping from one holiday party to another are such a menace in traffic. In hardened guzzlers who have alcohol in their blood twenty-four hours a day, moods seem to vary little. (In the latter connection, it is interesting to note that chronic alcoholics eventually lose some of their tolerance for alcohol, becoming stuporous with half as many drinks as they formerly required to make them drunk.)

Anyway, it is obvious that the different beverages do have different effects. A before-dinner Martini, because it is made of gin or vodka, begins to be felt almost immediately and delivers its maximum wallop within minutes, while a Manhattan, made of whiskey and vermouth, is slower and is felt for a longer time. It also is true that Scotch, because about three-fourths of its contents are neutral "grain whiskey," creeps up on you faster than a heavy bourbon.

A straight shot of bottled-in-bond whiskey irritates and shocks the stomach, causing that organ's walls to secrete mucus, which delays the drink's effect for several minutes. A couple of quick neat whiskies swallowed before dinner may not hit the drinker until he is halfway through his soup. But a water chaser will dilute whiskey enough to make it outdistance a Manhattan.

There is a popular saying with several conflicting versions, one of which goes:

Beer on whiskey,
Mighty risky;
Whiskey on beer,
Never fear.

The part that warns against beer following whiskey is right, because this combination of whiskey with a beer chaser (known as a Boilermaker) materially speeds and strengthens the whiskey's wallop. But the second part is probably wrong. It often takes a full hour to get the maximum effect from a few beers or glasses of wine. Whiskey taken later works faster and adds to the peak blood-alcohol level.

Still left unanswered are several more questions frequently asked about the effects of different potations. The answer to those about the congeners in spirits is saved for the following chapter, which deals with hangover. Do Martinis make you thirstier than other drinks do? It should be expected, from their higher alcoholic content, that the answer would be yes. And it is true that bitter drinks can make you hungry, while sweet mixers do the opposite.

This brings us to those thousands of individual stories that have a single plaintive pattern: "I can drink Scotch highballs all night long and never feel a thing, but bourbon gives me a headache." Or "I can drink all the bourbon I want, but Scotch always knocks me for a loop." Or "I can't drink beer," "I can't drink wine," or gimlets, daiquiris, stingers, fizzes, and so the tales go on endlessly.

Except for the guidance already offered, there is no clear answer to the foregoing, unless it involves allergies. And it well may, according to Dr. Theron Randolph of Chicago, who states that all alcoholic beverages "carry the allergenicity of the constituent foods from which they are derived." This researcher asserts that corn, wheat, barley, rye, potato, grape, beet, and cane-sugar allergies are involved in many individuals' reactions to specific alcoholic drinks. He says sensitivity to corn, in particular, is "one of the leading food allergies." Since Dr. Randolph's list covers every one of the raw materials used in making the most popular alcoholic beverages, this news conceivably can send large numbers of tipplers to consult allergists for advice about choosing drinks. There seems to be no question that at least a few individuals are made ill by some beverages, but can take others without apparent effects.

But the inexperienced drinker who becomes sick after a single cocktail need not be in a hurry to conclude that he has an allergy. More likely his stomach merely has been presented with a substance to which it is unaccustomed, and has reacted violently to the shock. In most cases the drink has been swallowed quickly, which is equivalent to whacking that organ with a board. The stomach usually becomes inured to the liquor after more doses on subsequent occasions.

Some complain only of hiccups, blaming the kind of beverage they have taken, when the real cause is simply that their stomachs are too full of food, liquid, or gas. The resulting pressure against the diaphragm causes spasms of that muscle and the "hic" that betrays gluttony. (The simplest cure, I have been told by a noted gastroenterologist, is to take a few deep breaths, then hold the breath for as long as possible. Another is to wrap a handkerchief around the tongue and pull that member until it hurts.)

Does a cigarette smoked while drinking multiply the intoxicating effect of the beverage? It may be noted that people, while imbibing freely, are inclined to smoke more than usual at the same time. It is convenient to blame the tobacco, of course, but nothing is known to suggest that it is guilty of adding to tipsification.

The first spur to vodka's meteoric rise to popularity in America was the claim that it is entirely "breathless," that a businessman could take any number of drinks at lunch and incur no risk of detection. A well-known private research agency actually conducted extensive smelling tests and confirmed that two drinks of vodka, compared to two whiskeys, were "practically imperceptible" on the drinker's breath. But anyone who has ever smelled vodka knows that although it has none of the aromas of other beverages, it also can be smelled by itself. To the sensitive nose of a nondrinker, too many vodka drinks are far from "breathless." In fact, law-enforcement agencies now commonly measure intoxication by simply measuring the alcoholic content of a drinker's breath.

There is danger in the deep-rooted belief that the first thing to do when someone faints or suffers shock, snakebite, or sunstroke, is to pour strong liquor down his gullet. The irritant effect of the liquor may cause him to show some momentary signs of stimulation (smelling salts would do the same), but since alcohol lowers his blood pressure, giving him a drink is one of the worst things to do.

Whether ardent spirits should be administered when a person has suffered a chill in freezing weather is also debatable. It is true that the feeling of chilliness is lessened by the flow of blood to his skin, but this actually causes his body to lose some of its heat. After a day on the ski slopes the glow a drink brings is pleasantly warming, but doctors forbid it for those chilled severely.

The only case recently on record in which alcohol helped to revive a freezing victim was reported from Michigan in 1959. A man was found frozen stiff beside a road in zero weather. Taken to a hospital, he amazed doctors by soon coming to life. They concluded that he had taken so many drinks before he passed out at the roadside that the alcohol in his blood had acted like antifreeze—that it actually had saved his life.

Does the fact that a drink loses some of your body's heat mean that this is the best way to cool off in extremely hot weather? No, answer the researchers, because although alcohol at first does reduce your temperature, your system promptly compensates by sending it up again. Besides, by making you feel warmer, it only adds to your discomfort. The less alcohol you put in your summer cold drinks, the cooler you will feel.

A debate long raging in Congress, intensified by the nuisance of tipsy air travelers, concerns the effect of liquor served in planes. In the early days of commercial flying it was believed that the slightest drink taken at high altitudes would send the drinker higher than the plane. Then tests were made of men drinking while breathing rarefied air. The results showed that altitude made little difference. It was explained that people breathe faster to get the oxygen they need, thereby increasing the amount of alcohol expelled from the blood by the lungs. This has not ended the controversy, however, and new regulations on sky-high drinking continue to flow from Washington. In 1960 the plane crews' unions finally succeeded in obtaining a rule that a passenger who brings his own hip flask to lighten the boredom of motionless hours in the stratosphere must hereafter turn it over to the stewardess and let her pour his drinks if she thinks he can hold them.

Now, to sort facts from fables concerning the role of alcohol in various diseases, let us begin with the common cold. Since nothing yet known seems able to cure this pesky ailment, the main question is whether any kind of nipping can make it worse. The unanimous medical answer is yes, because alcoholic drinks taken in excessive quantities increase fatigue and reduce the body's resistance to infection. Again, however, it is a matter of dosage, because the sedative, relaxing action of a single hot mulled wine or hot toddy at least can dull the patient's sense of discomfort. Whether the sweating they produce can stop a cold from developing is still unknown and seems doubtful. Anyhow, the medical profession has not yet disapproved of the traditional warming palliatives; some doctors still recommend them.

Without suggesting that the reader should engage in self-diagnosis or self-treatment, it also should be pointed out that thousands of physicians are prescribing measured daily doses of various alcoholic beverages for their patients who suffer from heart conditions; that experiments at the University of California have shown that certain wines reduce the amount of cholesterol in the liver, adrenals, and blood of animals; that the medical director of the Arthritis and Rheumatism Foundation has recommended a cocktail before dinner to help relieve the pain of arthritis, and that wines and other beverages have a long list of other accepted medical uses. Perhaps the most significant fact of all is that more and more investigators each year are reporting discoveries of relationships between emotional stress and the occurrence of not only heart diseases, but also of stomach and duodenal ulcers, and even of some types of cancer. These ulcers, by the way, are found oftener in abstainers than in heavy drinkers. Whether a daily drink or two can help prevent them is still supposition.

On the negative side there is a list of several diseases in which any kind of alcoholic drink is always sternly forbidden. It includes active acute nephritis; any hypermanic condition induced by medication, by fever, or by psychic disorder; conditions of severe psychic or physiological depression, and any ulcerous condition of the mouth or gastrointestinal tract that alcohol would irritate.

Are gout and liver cirrhosis caused by excessive drinking? Gout, which once was blamed on the drinking of port, has been found to be caused, instead, by an excess of uric acid in the blood. Perhaps its former association with this wine, favored by some of the English philosophers, evolved from gout's strange tendency to attack brilliant rather than ordinary men. Dramatizing the absolution of port as the cause of this ailment is the fact that some doctors now prescribe this wine in the treatment of their gouty patients, whose discomfort is eased thereby.

Liver cirrhosis ("hobnail liver"), on the other hand, is associated with excessive drinking, even though the cause of this ailment is still unknown. Cirrhosis actually occurs in far larger numbers of abstainers and moderate drinkers than in chronic drunkards, but nearly half of the latter have some liver disturbance. Because the rate at which cirrhosis occurs is nine times as high in heavy drinkers as in the rest of the populace, some connection is apparent from the statistics.

The diseases of chronic alcoholism—polyneuropathy, dropsy, and pellagra—are now known to be caused by dietary deficiencies; in other words, by the alcoholic's failure to eat an adequate diet. Each of these occurs also in undernourished people who use no alcohol, and each responds readily to the administration of vitamins. Even when a heavy drinker eats as much as a normal person, he still is starved, because he needs an enormous supply of extra vitamins and proteins to balance the calories he gets from alcohol. Alcohol itself causes no damage to any vital organ, because the blood never contains enough of it to produce direct injury. But present medical opinion is that long-continued excessive use when the drinker is undernourished, and particularly when the traumatic experience of intoxication is continually repeated, can result in damage to the central nervous system.

Fear of these afflictions, allayed by the spectacle of obvious carefree enjoyment of beer, wine, and liquor by millions of healthy people throughout the land, leaves most thoughtful Americans confused about drinks and drinking. Many are wondering what or whom to believe on these subjects. The flood of popular psychology and do-it-yourself psychiatry has made many a young mother apprehensive lest her children, if not breast-fed, will turn out to be drunkards. Much of the old folklore about drinking still is widely believed; the latter is merely an example of the new.

Nobody yet knows for certain what causes compulsive drinking. The current scientific vogue is to say that there is no one cause, that there are many. Whether heredity plays a part is doubted by most researchers, although emotional and mental abnormalities occur more frequently in some families than in others. Experiments with different strains of mice have yielded some that liked alcohol better than the others, but it is not suggested that this implies anything about humans. Some researchers speculate that there are mysterious chemical causes, perhaps a mysterious "X" factor in body chemistry, or insufficient or excessive output of the vital substances produced by the ductless glands. Dr. Randolph, the Chicago allergist, suspects allergies as a cause, submitting that individuals' sensitivity to specific foods leads to their addiction to those foods. Others have blamed "momism" (overprotective mothers), another has suggested "the lack of popism" (cold, unresponsive fathers), and still others blame sexual repression. The W.C.T.U. insists that anyone who drinks enough, often enough, inevitably becomes addicted to drink. Psychiatrists, scoffing at this, say that a compulsive drinker has a crippled personality, that he is a person with low tolerance for psychic pain, that he cannot bear to face normal frustrations, and is impelled to drug himself to escape reality. Some even state that the potential addict can be recognized at an early age; that if he never begins to drink, he eventually will become a problem in some other way, and that every compulsive drinker is a person who has crossed the path of his nemesis. There may be some connection with religious, ethnic, or national groups' cultural patterns, a subject discussed in the later chapter on manners.

Complicating the subject even further is the fact that there are many intoxicants besides alcohol. The fumes of gasoline, paint thinner, and benzedrine produce dizziness and intoxicated behavior. Even the oxygen in the air intoxicates; anyone who breathes deeply through his mouth has learned it. Nutmeg and mace have been banned from the kitchens of American prisons because inmates made themselves drunk by mixing them with hot water, tea, or coffee. Both of these spices contain nutmeg oil, a nerve sedative with such narcotic power that it causes excitement, delirium, and even death. There have been addicts to ether, chloroform, and nitrous oxide ("laughing gas")—in fact, to almost anything that can numb the sense of awareness. A London medical journal reported in 1959 the strange cases of seven men and two women "hydrolics" who were addicted to drinking water, regularly became drunk on it, and suffered hangovers afterward.

How deeply in human nature the origins of intoxication lie is suggested by Dr. Edwin Loeb in *Culture in History,* a publication of the Columbia University Press. Ethnologist Loeb, studying the ways of primitive races, has concluded that prehistoric man, long before he discovered how to make alcoholic drinks, learned to make himself drunk by chewing toxic plants —that, in other words, the use of narcotics came long before drinking.

This chapter of facts and fables has covered so wide a range of miscellany that by now its intended purpose may seem obscure. The point it simply attempts to make is that the truths about drinks and drinking are vastly outnumbered by the fables and fallacies of folklore, and that those who use beer, wine, or spirits should believe only that which has been thoroughly sifted, weighed, and found to be true.

There is one addition to the newer fables; it comes from Soviet Russia. A Radio Moscow announcer has commented as follows on excessive drinking:

"In capitalist countries men drink from despair in order to forget how they are exploited, their bad working conditions, and the specter of unemployment. But the alcoholism of the Soviet citizen has other causes: it comes essentially from the overflowing joy of living and from his tendency to celebrate with spirit the great achievements of socialism."

CHAPTER 12

Truth About Hangover

JOKES ABOUT HANGOVER, THE GRIM AFTERMATH OF OVERINDULgence, evoke no laughter in hospitals, jails, or in the research institutions where its symptoms are being studied. As one of the leading causes of accidents, hung-over drivers and industrial workers probably cost as many lost limbs and lives as are caused by those who have just been guzzling.

Nor are hangover agonies, although a source of huge amusement to disgustingly healthy people, at all funny to the recent carouser with his splitting headache, searing thirst, furry tongue, pounding heart, fluttering stomach, terrifying pains, chills, shakiness, and screaming jitters.

The curious mythology of drinking contains more fallacies and untruths about antidotes and preventives for morning-after misery than about any other aspect of inebriety. These myths obscure hangover's simple cause: too much alcohol.

Exactly what is hangover? It is a topsy-turvy condition of the entire human being, in which his brain and nervous system have been partially paralyzed for a number of hours and have failed to control the body's chemistry in their usual way. The alcohol has already been eliminated, but his body's chemical balance has been upset, his digestive organs have been abused, and he feels overpowering fatigue in his every muscle.

The sufferer's insatiable thirst most clearly illustrates his system's chemical imbalance. He craves gallons of water, although his body has not dried out. The human body is about 80 per cent water. Approximately a third of it is inside the cells, whose water content fluctuates like the tides. Intoxication causes the cells to lose part of their water, thus producing the sensation of thirst.

Too much smoking, too much eating, too much expended energy, and going too long without sleep—or any one of these excesses—can also produce a hangover, even without any drinking. The person who has drunk too much usually has committed most or all of these at the same time. Each added abuse compounds the total effect.

Attendant tortures are remorse, fear, and anxiety. Morning-after realization of foolish behavior the night before adds the psychic pain of guilt feelings to the frightening physical symptoms. These mental miseries of hangover are worst of all in the addictive drinker. The trouble he originally drowned with alcohol now returns, looming bigger than before. This may have something to do with his continued binges.

In a scientifically controlled experiment at an eastern university, several men were placed in rooms by themselves and instructed to drink until they were dead drunk. They awoke thirsty and fatigued, but, having indulged in no other excesses, and feeling neither guilt nor fear, not one complained of even the usual headache.

To convince drinkers of these truths is something of a problem. One awakens feeling nauseated and says, "I was sober as a judge all evening, so it must have been something I ate." It turns out he had a cocktail with hors d'oeuvres, then wine with a heavy dinner—combinations that slowed the absorption of alcohol into his blood—followed by a snifter of brandy, which the food in his stomach also held back for a time. Although at no time had he felt "high," his irritated stomach made him sick in the morning.

Another reveler once said: "I went to bed feeling just fine, but I woke up feeling lousy. It must have been the sleep that did it."

Naturally, the average celebrant feels no pain at the end of a hilarious evening, because he is still anesthetized by his drinks. But their anesthetic effect has worn off completely before morning, and when he awakens he feels the aftermath.

While his hangover lasts, the victim tries a weird assortment of cures. These range from raw egg with tabasco sauce in milk (a "prairie oyster") to pea soup, black coffee, laxatives, Turkish baths, and long walks. None of these does him the slightest good. The coffee is a mistake because the patient is fatigued and could benefit most from sleep. To give him a stimulant is like whipping a tired horse. The Turkish-bath treatment is also fallacious because the body has already oxidized the alcohol; and even if there were some left, only infinitesimal amounts can be lost by sweating. Walking is wrong, too, because what he needs is rest, not exercise. Something alkaline to help quiet his roaring stomach, a couple of aspirins to dull his pain, and going to bed are by far the best things to do.

But usually, during a hangover, the jittery, nerve-shattered victim can no longer sleep. Sometimes a doctor prescribes a sedative for him. One kind of sedation *not* to use at this time is that of more alcohol. Of course "a hair of the dog that bit you" can dull hangover pain, but it is foolish to take another drink at this time. It can start the whole traumatic cycle again.

Nothing—absolutely nothing—*cures* a hangover, except time.

There is a widely believed fable that a drink of water taken the morning after a spree makes the thirsty man drunk all over again. What really happens is that the water, taken while he is still drowsy, awakens him; he discovers he is dizzy, and mistakes his dizziness for intoxication. Whether he drank water or not, he would have been dizzy anyway.

Having recovered from his last gruesome experience, the frequent imbiber still refuses to accept facts, but clings to another common fallacy—that there are ways to *prevent* a hangover.

One currently popular "preventive" actually sounds plausible at first blush. Since thirst, weakness, pain, and acidosis are all parts of a binge's aftermath, all that seemingly should be necessary is to take remedies in advance of the malady. Before going out to tie one on, an advocate of this method places beside his bed a glass of pineapple juice (vitamin C) with added vitamins B1 and B2, two aspirin tablets, and two antacid pills. When he eventually staggers home, he swallows all of these before retiring. If he has drunk enough, however, the dawn still produces morning-after distress. But his faith in his "preventive" remains unshaken. He concludes somebody must have poisoned his liquor.

Some people imagine that the best antidote for tomorrow's hangover is to sober up the carouser tonight. This leads to some rather gruesome treatments. The gentler ones include cold towels, dousing the head, fresh air, a slap in the face, a sudden fright, and a cold shower. In colonial days flogging and bleeding were considered helpful.

Eating after drinking, in an attempt to absorb the alcohol, is also useless. Eating before or with drinks only counteracts their peak intoxicating effect, not their aftereffects. Vomiting can get rid of a drink, of course—if it is done in time. Oxygen may help slightly in the sobering process, by increasing the small amount of alcohol exhaled in the breath. Certain amino acids are said to be capable of accelerating (to a minor degree) the oxidation of alcohol by the liver, but only when they are injected intravenously. A stimulant, such as coffee or benzedrine, only keeps the besotted member awake, which is dangerous because it may encourage him to drive his car. Putting him to sleep with a sedative is worst of all; with this on top of the alcohol, he may never wake up.

Millions are firmly convinced that different kinds of drinks produce different kinds of hangover—that there is a typical champagne hangover, a gin hangover, a Scotch hangover, and so on. Their testimony consists of relating isolated incidents concerning which their memories are foggy. They remember what they drank, but forget how much, and fail to consider that the different drinks differ considerably in strength. There conceivably may be some minor variations in degrees of gastric or other kinds of local irritation, but this is mere conjecture. Except for busy kidneys from large volumes of beer, there as yet is no solid evidence to connect any special morning-after symptoms with any particular beverage.

Discussions of drinks that supposedly produce more or less hangover revolve mostly around whiskeys—specifically about their "congeners." At least half of the bartenders in the nation will tell you flatly that hangover headaches after drinking whiskey are caused only by these "congeners." The rest of the barkeeps will probably answer that the "congener-headache" story is only propaganda spread by a certain maker of blended whiskeys, who is trying to convert drinkers of straight bourbon and rye into customers for his spirit blends. The latter group are right, but the former are not necessarily wrong. The truth is that nobody really knows.

What are these "congeners," with their purported extra headache potential? They are the hundreds of flavor substances in alcoholic beverages—mainly those (other than alcohol and carbon dioxide) that are formed during fermentation. All of the beverages (including beer, wine, all kinds of whiskey, gin, rum, brandy, and vodka) contain congeners in microscopic amounts. But the straight whiskeys have more than twice as much as the "blended whiskeys" do—and about this the battle rages.

The main congener is called fusel oil; it consists principally of the higher alcohols—amyl, butyl, and propyl. Other congeners include furfural, esters, and aldehydes. Fusel oil has no recognizable smell of its own, but in new whiskeys it produces a full, ether-like sensation in your nose. An aged whiskey gets new flavors from the wooden barrel, which cover up the fusel-oil taste. The barrel does not absorb it; there is as much in old whiskey as in new. Actually, distillers remove most of the fusel oil during distillation and sell it for paint solvent, but they purposely leave a fractional amount in their whiskey. It would not taste like whiskey without it. "Congeners," one distiller says, "are as important to whiskey as bacteria is to cheese."

In the autumn of 1936 a strange experiment was conducted in an isolated region of the Adirondacks. Ten business and professional men in their thirties were paid to take a six-week vacation of hiking, hunting, and boating, with one condition: that they would get drunk three nights a week—sufficiently drunk to be hung-over the following morning. While producing the agreed grand total of one hundred and eighty hangovers, the ten men were constantly tested physically, mentally, and emotionally. Even their movements while sleeping, their urine volume, and their handwriting were recorded, but especially their hangover symptoms. The results: a spirit blend, drunk alternately with three straight whiskies, produced the minimum in aftereffects.

This occasioned no surprise whatever on the part of the whiskey blender who had paid the bills for the whole experiment. In fact, while it went on, he was already planning his advertising, which soon was shouting in brochures to the trade: "Less hangover! Less upset! Less jitters! Less head!" for his brand of blended whiskey. His competitors, however, objected, and the government soon put a stop to his advertising.

From scientists in research institutions promptly came assorted sarcastic comments, pooh-poohing the "congener-headache" theory. The miscroscopic amount of congeners in any whiskey is far too small, most of them said, to produce even the slightest headache. Measurements showed that no whiskey contains any more than one hundredth of one per cent of anything but ethyl alcohol and water.

Nevertheless, the battle continues. Experiments with congeners on rats were still going on in 1959 at the Medical College of Virginia. The results, as usual, were still inconclusive: "The role which the congeners might play in the over-all pharmacologic action of whiskey remains largely to be determined."

On the main aspects of mornings after, however, all recognized authorities are in complete agreement. With or without headaches, a hangover is a distressing, traumatic experience. Its symptoms result from an upset of the body's chemical balance. There is no cure for it except time. Its only preventive is not to drink excessively. And its simple cause is too much alcohol.

CHAPTER 13

For Wise Hosts and Guests

THIS CHAPTER IS FOR HOSTS WHO GUARD THEIR BUDGETS OR THEIR furniture, and for guests who enjoy a drink but not a spree. It discusses some of the problems frequently encountered by those who themselves use alcoholic beverages sensibly. These people are in the majority; their behavior and that of their friends is mainly temperate, but they also come into contact with others of whom this is not true.

A young matron wrote me, after reading my book about wines: "Before we were married, we went with a hard-drinking crowd. My husband and I don't care for liquor, and we have none in the house. We'd like to invite these old friends over for a party, but we can't give them what they're accustomed to drink unless we buy a whole assortment of expensive liquors. Isn't there some other solution?"

This couple's problem was readily solved. They held a barbecue on a hot Saturday afternoon and served beer and red wine coolers. Under the circumstances nobody expected to be offered strong drinks.

Considerably more perplexing is the dilemma of home owners who sometimes attend hilarious cocktail parties given by acquaintances and business friends. They feel compelled to reciprocate occasionally, but hate to contemplate doing so in their own homes. The thought of stepped-on canapés soiling their rugs, wet glasses staining the piano, and noisy celebrants annoying their neighbors is simply too forbidding.

Under still greater pressure are those suburbanites, members of social groups in which each couple takes regular turns at hosting the rest, who find that the successive gatherings are growing excessively liquid.

Instead of hiring a hall and a professional caterer, a few things can be done at least to minimize the damage of such parties held at home. One is to hold down the potency of the drinks that are served. Reducing the quantity of total alcohol that all the guests consume reduces the frequency and degree of alcoholized behavior by the raucous few.

A remarkably effective furniture-saving device is the automatic liquor dispenser, a gadget currently on the market that attaches to a bottle and measures out exactly one ounce of spirits for each drink. (Another brand dispenses one and a half ounces, which still is less than the two-ounce jolt many overliberal hosts put into their highballs and cocktails.) If only to ensure success with a mixing recipe, liquor always needs to be measured, never poured out with a heavy hand.

But isn't it considered pinchpenny to serve liquor that doesn't taste strong? It is true that many nervous or obtrusive hosts confuse generosity with hospitality, flaunting their affluence with: "Here, let me freshen up that sissy drink for you." But the considerate home bartender does not slug his guests' drinks. He knows that most people control only the *number* of drinks they take, seldom considering their alcoholic strength. In this respect he is responsible for the way they will feel the following day.

Moreover, a highball made with one ounce of whiskey need not taste weak if a moderate-sized glass is used, nor does a Martini lack flavor if sufficient vermouth is included in the mix.

Another measure that helps preserve decorum is to use the 80- or 86-proof whiskeys, gins, rums, brandies, or vodkas wherever these types of liquor are called for. The new brands of less potent spirits lack none of the basic flavors of the earlier 90- and 100-proof versions; only the alcohol content is less.

Cocktails need to be mixed long and vigorously to get them properly diluted by melting ice, as the recipe books require. To reduce further the jolt people feel from their liquor, the food served at the party should be high in protein and moderately oily. (Meat, sausage, egg, and fish tidbits, cheese dips and spreads, and nuts best serve this purpose; pretzels, breadstuffs, and popcorn do not.)

By these precautionary measures the host has done all he reasonably can for his guests, including the reckless ones.

What can be done, however, about the bibulous late arrival who comes to the party already lubricated, and whom another libation or two would turn into a behavior problem? Such company puts any host on his mettle. The first thing to do is to be certain that all bottles in sight are tightly corked, so that the new arrival will not be inclined to help himself. (It is not a good idea to let such people mix their own drinks; that informal way of supplying beverages belongs in groups where all members are obviously temperate.) The tipsy guest should be served something well-diluted; and when he comes back for more, the host does well to busy himself with washing glasses, getting more ice cubes, or filling trays with food. Every device must be employed to keep the inebriated member from drinking any more. It may also be well to enlist some friends to take away his car keys and drive him home.

Important for any such occasion is to have plenty of soft drinks on hand for those who are "on the wagon." It is a cruel host indeed who forces the first alcoholic drink on a shy individual who is taking the cure. In fact, no matter how anxious the man of the house may be to thaw things out at his party, it is the exact reverse of hospitality to insist that any guest take an extra drink he doesn't want. If someone is hurt or killed in an automobile accident later in the evening, the host is an accessory to the crime.

Some of these points apply, too, when guests come to dinner. When the meal is long delayed and too many drinks are taken into empty stomachs, some may no longer be in a condition to enjoy a culinary masterpiece. In addition to regulating the strength of what is drunk, the key solution is to have the meal ready early. Experienced hosts allow not much over a half-hour for predinner drinking and relaxed, friendly chatting. They never let it get beyond an hour, and do not extend it for guests who arrive late.

People with slender budgets, no matter how temperate their friends are, find the high cost of liquors is a serious problem. Their solution is in aiming for flavor and glamour instead of alcoholic strength, because the glorification of any beverage is mainly a matter of publicity and the way it is presented. Expensive spirits can be stretched and made more flavorful by using recipes (available at most dealers) that call for such ingredients as fruit juices, grenadine, and wines. Many a skillful host uses them to mix a single cocktail that he introduces as his personal specialty. An easily prepared example is this inexpensive, but rather potent favorite among wine hobbyists: equal parts of white wine, sherry, dry vermouth, sweet vermouth, and brandy, aged for a day or two in the refrigerator and served from a cocktail shaker. This drink alone can be served at a modest cocktail party held at home.

Especially impressive when only one kind of drink is served is a champagne punch, which gets most of its volume from nonalcoholic and low-potency ingredients and its glamour from a single bottle of champagne added at the final moment before serving.

In fact, champagne served alone or as a cocktail is a relatively moderate before-dinner drink, compared to strong cocktails and liquor highballs, and is easy on the budget because only single bottles need to be purchased instead of a costly assortment.

This applies especially to wedding receptions, which San Francisco columnist Paul Speegle once described as "cocktail parties with orange blossoms." An inexpensive bulk-fermented champagne, purchased at the discount offered by the case, suits this purpose admirably.

Dinners with wine are naturally temperate because food reduces the alcoholic effect. The host serves small glasses of an apéritif, such as sherry, announcing that wine is being served with the meal. An extra flourish can be provided by a flaming dessert, which is achieved simply by adding an ounce or two of warm rum or brandy and lighting it with a match.

The need to entertain people who drop in casually raises the question of always keeping a well-stocked bar. One way to hold down the assortment is to have on hand a supply of beer, sherry, port, bottled Martini and Manhattan cocktails, and a whiskey or brandy for visitors who prefer a highball. The simplest beverage stock of all is a single decanter of sherry or port kept on the sideboard.

The minimum liquor assortment for a full-fledged invitational cocktail party, however, consists of Martinis, Manhattans (which require gin, American whiskey, dry and sweet vermouths), and both Scotch and American whiskeys for highballs. Other necessary beverage supplies include pitted green olives for Martinis, maraschino cherries for Manhattans, soda, ginger ale, and extra ice.

Any householder who has very many hard-drinking, gregarious friends is wise to avoid keeping a large stock of liquor on hand. If they pay him a visit during one of their roaring weekends, they may stay as long as there is anything left to drink.

Not only hosts have problems; guests have them too. Businessmen, in particular, are expected to drink with their customers, and anyone who is not clutching a glass at a drinking occasion is uncomfortably conspicuous. It is impossible to drink water while clients are working their way through two or three Martinis or bourbons on the rocks. So the businessman learns to order unobtrusively a glass of Calso, soda, or quinine water with a slice of lime, or a Bloody Mary without the vodka, or a "horse's neck," which professional bartenders know as meaning ginger ale with a curlicue of lemon. These things look enough like a highball to get the nondrinker by.

The neophyte drinker who sips a single highball in a restaurant or bar has some preliminary idea of its potency and can be reasonably sure of getting home unscathed. But when he accepts such a drink from a home bartender, he does well to learn, before he swallows it, how much liquor it contains. A zealous host is definitely not to be trusted to determine the dose of alcohol a guest shall imbibe.

An experienced guest who does not care for a drink at a home affair sometimes asks for a highball with a pony (one ounce) of liquor instead of with a jigger (an ounce and a half). He knows how to nurse the same drink through the evening, sometimes visiting the bar to ask that the half-empty glass be again filled with soda. This is an effective way to avoid letting an insistent host refill it with liquor. In an especially difficult situation, the contents can go into the nearest potted plant.

It is recorded that in ancient Babylon, during the reign of

King Hammurabi, tavern keepers who dispensed drinks with short measure were punished by being drowned, an effective way of preventing them from repeating the offense. When a modern bartender does this for someone who has had too much, he is doing the guest a favor.

CHAPTER 14

How to Drink and Stay Thin

WAISTLINE-CONSCIOUS PEOPLE WHO USE ANY ALCOHOLIC BEVERages face a minor dilemma every time they contemplate taking a sip. They have to decide what portion of which food they will do without for each drink they take in.

For alcohol is rich in calories. How rich? A bottle of beer contains as much as a cup of whole milk. A three-ounce glass of claret almost equals a medium-sized apple. A jigger of whiskey, gin, rum, brandy, or vodka is more than equal to two pats of butter.

Yet many calorie-watchers use these various beverages and keep their figures slim at the same time. Most stage and screen people, whose incomes depend on keeping their silhouettes from bulging, manage it successfully throughout their careers. Weight-watching, all authorities agree, is mainly a matter of arithmetic.

To keep a trim figure, almost everybody nowadays realizes, you have to hold down the total number of calories ingested from all the foods and beverages you consume during a day. Reducing pills, machines sold to roll off your fat, and slenderizing breads whose only virtue is that their slices are thinner, have been shown to have little or no real weight-controlling value. Every experienced dieter knows that he must obey the advice of his handy calorie chart and the ABC rules of normal exercise and nutrition. When he eats an extra slice of toast at breakfast, or takes a cocktail before dinner, he simply deletes from his day's intake something else of equivalent caloric value.

Accordingly, an alcohol-calorie chart that lists the approximate fuel values of most of the popular drinks is contained at the end of this chapter.

There are a few additional things about wines, beers, and liquors that those who use them in slimming regimes ought to know. One is about the extra importance of maintaining a balanced diet. Alcohol is a food, in the sense that it delivers energy. But pure alcohol and the distilled spirits contain none of the vitamins, proteins, and minerals that the body needs to keep healthy. Beer and wine contain certain vitamins and other food substances, but the more alcohol a person consumes, the more vitamins and proteins he requires to balance the alcohol calories. People who purposely eat sparingly when they drink need to be certain that what they *do* eat gives them this vitamin-protein-calorie balance.

Alcohol does not actually become fat, but it is fattening anyway. What happens is that the body burns the alcohol calories first, using them for fuel. Other food calories thus are not needed for that purpose, and are spared and stored as fat. This is why the calories you get from alcohol add as much to your avoirdupois as those from ham and eggs, sandwiches, or bonbons.

Something else to keep in mind is that some drinks can stimulate your appetite and tempt you to overeat. Dry table wines, because they are faintly bitter, especially have this effect, to such an extent that many doctors prescribe them for patients whose appetites are sluggish. The bitter herbs in apéritifs and the bitter substances in beer (obtained from lupulin) have some of this quality, too. (Alcohol alone depresses appetite, but these bitter beverages add to your hunger more than their alcohol takes away.)

Moreover, when alcohol relaxes your inhibitions, it may weaken your resolve to stick to your diet. "I'll cut out dessert tonight," you promise yourself, as you inhale the oily hors d'oeuvres. Later in the evening, however, the tray of confections the waiter brings looks just too tempting to be resisted.

Isn't there some way to depress your appetite instead of sharpening it? Yes, there is, and strangely enough it is the higher-caloried sweet drinks that can do it. Sugar reduces your desire for food. The trouble here is in making certain that the extra calories taken aboard in the form of alcohol and sweetening do not overbalance those that a dulled appetite refuses.

In 1958 a group of alcohol researchers experimented with wine as a means of combating obesity's number one hazard, the bedtime snack. Subjects who were in the habit of raiding the refrigerator late at night were encouraged to have wine with their dinners. Close observation of their movements showed that their nocturnal overeating was materially reduced, and in some instances was discontinued. This may possibly be explained by the recent findings of nutritionists that both animals and humans tend to decrease their carbohydrate intake whenever they increase their intake of wine. Evidence of this is furnished by the typical Italian in Italy, who gets fully one-tenth of his calories from his daily half-liter (about a pint) of red table wine, without becoming overweight.

Another explanation is that overeating is usually caused by emotional tension. Wine and beer relieve tension and thereby reduce craving for unneeded food.

Both wine and beer are often included in reducing diets prescribed by physicians. Beer especially fits this use because it is more filling than other drinks and because the drinker who once learns that a bottle contains about 170 calories finds it easy to perform his calorie arithmetic.

The classic argument over whether beer is "fattening" has been the subject of repeated disputes between brewers and government officials who scan beer advertising. An adman who studied calorie charts noted that milk, which usually is not considered especially caloric, is considerably richer in calories than beer. He created the phrase "dietetically non-fattening," which sold millions of bottles of his client's brand of brew before the government, which felt that the public failed to understand what "dietetically" meant, persuaded him to stop.

Obviously, the best way to control calories from drinks is to take the long, well-diluted kinds that you drink slowly, such as highballs in preference to cocktails. But first make sure that whoever mixes them does not slosh too big a dose of Scotch or bourbon (65 to 80 calories per ounce) into your glass. Sweet mixers should be avoided. Four ounces of ginger ale or 3 ounces of cola represent 40 calories each, while the caloric content of club soda or water is zero. White wine and soda is often favored because it looks like a highball and has a long sipping time. Three ounces of dry white table wine amount to 66 calories; champagne contains 75.

A fortunate development for dieters is the current trend toward lower-proof distilled spirits. Since all of the calories in whiskey, rum, vodka, or any unsweetened liquor are in its alcohol content, the new 80-proof spirits are one-fifth less fattening than the 100-proof bonded liquors. Anybody who has switched to vodka only because the 80-proof vodka brands contain fewer calories than most whiskeys, can switch back now to whiskeys, which now come at 80-proof, too.

CALORIE VALUES OF ALCOHOLIC DRINKS

	Quantity	*Calories*
Beer, average	12 oz. bottle	172
Table wines, champagnes	3 oz. glass	66 to 78
Appetizer and dessert wines	3 oz. glass	114 to 144
*Distilled spirits, 90 proof	1 jigger (1½ oz.)	110
**Highballs, water or soda	(1½ oz. spirits)	110
Highballs, ginger ale	(1½ oz. spirits)	150
Tom Collins, soda	(1½ oz. gin; lemon, sugar)	154
Cuba Libre	(2 oz. rum; lime, cola)	200
Mint Julep	(4 oz. bourbon; sugar, mint)	320
Manhattan	(1½ oz. whiskey, ¾ oz. sweet vermouth)	145
Martini (2 to 1)	(1 oz. gin, ¾ oz. dry vermouth)	140
Martini (10 to 1)	(2¼ oz. gin, 1/20 oz. dry vermouth)	170
Old Fashioned	(1½ oz. whiskey; sugar, fruit)	130
Whiskey or Brandy Sour	(1½ oz. spirits; sugar, lemon juice)	140
Daiquiri	(1½ oz. rum; sugar, lime juice)	160
Liqueurs, 60 to 110 proof	1 oz.	94 to 170
Brandy (86 proof) used as liqueur	1 oz.	71

* Whiskey, gin, brandy, rum, vodka, aquavit, tequila. Add 12 calories per jigger if 100 proof spirits are used; subtract 5 if spirits are 86 proof; subtract 12 if spirits are 80 proof.

** If 2 oz. of spirits used, one-third more calories are added.

NOTE: The beer figure is from an article by Earl D. Stewart in *American Brewer*. Those for wines are from the University of California Department of Viticulture and Enology. The values for highballs and cocktails are for drinks mixed with spirits of 90-proof strength.

Incidentally, weight-watchers need not worry about calories from alcoholic beverages used in cooking. When sufficient heat is applied, the alcohol evaporates, and all that remains is the flavor.

How to drink and stay thin boils down, then, to simple addition and subtraction. If you add a cocktail, subtract the dessert. If you take a glass of sherry, delete one slice of buttered bread.

And if your arithmetic is weak, or your will power is lacking, don't be surprised when the host asks: "What'll you have, my plump friend?"

CHAPTER 15

Liquor for Children

NO POLITICALLY MINDED JUDGE OR POLICE OFFICER WOULD DARE to advocate publicly that American parents should teach their children how to drink at home. Privately, however, a considerable number of public officials think it would be an excellent idea.

Since in many states it is legally a crime to give any underage person an alcoholic beverage, this obviously is a delicate subject. Nevertheless, a few social scientists have been rash enough to broach it, thereby shocking and enraging considerable numbers of people.

Before tangling directly with wrathful opponents of the idea, let us see how the younger set is dealing with intoxicants currently.

"There isn't drinking at all teenage parties—only at about 60 per cent of them," says a high-school student in San Francisco. A high-school survey in Utah has shown that 26 per cent of a group of sophomores had been "high" during the month preceding their interviews. Teenagers in southern Florida are reported bringing vodka to school with their lunches, going out to their cars to take a swallow at recess. A seventeen-year-old girl died and three boys made themselves seriously ill by drinking antifreeze at a Christmas party in Massachusetts. In many states college students cheering their athletic teams to victory are seen eating oranges they have injected earlier with liquor, using syringes. Fraternity houses without bars, secret or open, are a rarity nationally.

Not all youngsters become intoxicated from beer, wine, or liquor. Wichita Falls, Texas, police reported in 1959 that as many as one fourth of that city's 16,000 teenagers were endangering their lives by sniffing the fumes of plastic cement for "kicks" during school hours. The custom had been introduced by students disciplined earlier for drinking. In the same year the Federal Food and Drug Administration banned over-the-counter sales of amphetamine-based nasal inhalers in the nation's drugstores because children were buying them as substitutes for alcohol. Tranquilizer pills have a ready market among juveniles whose parents have banished drinking from their parties.

Needless to say, the foregoing are isolated conditions. The actual situation, most authorities agree, is that the majority of young people of high-school age in the United States use alcoholic beverages on occasion, and that most of them have parental permission to do so. In fact, only a small percentage use beer as often as once a week, and a still smaller segment use whiskey, gin, rum, or vodka frequently. Further, there is evidence that nearly nine tenths of all delinquent children show signs of being in trouble before they are eleven years of age, half of them before they are eight. This would indicate that drinking as a factor in juvenile delinquency is more a manifestation than a cause.

Nevertheless, most members of our younger generation do drink (even though it is generally against the law) and this is what we are discussing.

Why they engage in clandestine tippling—the use of alcohol without their parents' approval—has been the subject of numerous inquiries. Parental example and the availability of beer, wine, and liquor in their communities are the explanations offered by "drys," who would solve the problem by prohibiting the sale of all intoxicants. Youthful curiosity and social pressure in teenage groups are suggested as causes by those who made the survey in Utah. High-school students themselves answer the question: "Kids will think you're nuts if you're different." "You want to be like the others, your clothes the same, your car not too radical; if you're different you're an outcast." "If you won't take a drink they call you 'chicken.' "

Among boys another motive for heavy drinking is identified. It is every youth's intense desire to be considered a man. Semanticist S. I. Hayakawa, a student of adolescent psychology, points out that historically in all societies there have been initiation rites and tests for boys to prove their manhood. "Now," he says, "they have to heist a car, sabotage somebody's lawn, or drink one another under the table." (Dr. Hayakawa suggests encouraging boys to take physically challenging jobs or to engage in rough outdoor sports as healthier ways to prove their virility.)

Even toddlers seek to emulate their cocktail-drinking elders, and cry in restaurants until their parents order them "mocktails" or "Shirley Temples."

The lure of anything that is forbidden, the perverse motivation of humans classically illustrated by Adam and Eve, also gets occasional mention. To take a prohibited drink is one of the easiest means of rebellion for the teenager, to whom anything worth doing is also worth overdoing.

Here school instruction concerning alcohol, required by law in most of the states, plays an influential role. Reputable schoolbook publishers issue texts that lump alcohol with morphine, heroin, and opium. Unless the schools dare risk the ire of prohibitionists, they must teach the subject in ways implying frighteningly that a single drink is the first step toward the inevitable fate of a habitual drunkard.

A favorite story among those who ridicule this kind of education concerns an anti-alcohol lecturer who exhibited to a group of children a live worm, a bottle half full of water, and a bottle of gin. He placed the worm in the water, and the creature continued to wriggle. Then he filled the bottle with gin, and the worm promptly curled up, motionless. "Now, children, what does that show?" he asked the class.

A youngster raised his hand. "It looks like if I drink a lot of gin," he said, "I won't have any worms."

The majority of pupils who are taught in school that alcohol is a deadly poison observe their mothers sipping cocktails and their fathers taking beer or highballs without outward signs of injury. The youthful desire to experiment on themselves is thereby only heightened.

The association of drinking with sin may be one of the most potent intemperance-breeding factors of all. Studies of Irish-Americans, who have the highest incidence of addictive drinking found in any ethnic group in the nation, reveal that the use of alcoholic beverages by their children is generally forbidden. A study of drinking in colleges has shown that the problem drinkers among students come oftenest from a background of attempted total prohibition. The low rates observed among Italians and Jews are related to the fact that they drink as a matter of course from early childhood, attaching no importance to the act.

Yet the prevailing American attitude toward alcohol is obviously one of guilt. It is exhibited almost daily in the press, where liquor still is regularly referred to as "booze"—an expression that betrays an individual's guilty feeling about his own drinking if he drinks at all. As long as becoming drunk is regarded as wicked (to paraphrase Oscar Wilde's comment on war), it will always have its fascination; but when it comes to be looked upon as vulgar, it will lose some of its popularity.

It is apparent from the history of smoking that merely denouncing a practice does not stop it. Even drinking has not been damned in recent years as vociferously as cigarettes have been on the front pages of every newspaper in the nation. Yet 1959 cigarette consumption was the highest in the nation's history. If American children had believed the condemnations of alcoholic beverages that have been addressed to them for generations, the majority of American adults would now be teetotalers, instead of the exact reverse.

Some parents do teach their children to drink, and sometimes they regret it later. Especially is this true of mothers who introduce liquor to girls going away to college, to tell them "what to expect" when they have been drinking. A comment on this is furnished by Dr. Albert Ullman, professor of sociology at Tufts University, who states that the *later* the age at which members of a group are introduced to alcohol, the higher the group's incidence of preaddictive conditions. He adds that people who drink excessively are least likely to have had their first drink at home and in the company of their parents. Dr. Ullman concludes by suggesting that children may be "vaccinated" against addiction:

"Psychological conditions suitable for developing addiction are created in groups whose drinking customs are poorly integrated with the total culture. . . . Small, frequent doses of alcohol, beginning early in the child's life, may be what is required to make alcohol psychologically unavailable as an addictive substance."

Another nationally known authority, who asks that he not

be identified, writes in a personal communication as follows:

"We teach children how to cook, sew, vote, drive, get a job, and make a living. We teach them almost everything except how to handle the one thing that, next to automobiles, offers the most opportunity to get them into trouble—alcohol. Every person who is going to be a normal drinker has to learn what to expect from it, and the best place to learn this is under home conditions. Every young girl, in particular, should know her capacity before she ever drinks in public, so that she will not have to experiment and exceed it. Children do drink—that is known beyond any question; it is no longer an issue. The only issue is whether they shall learn at home, or at a party where it is forbidden, or on the back seat of someone's car."

This book does not attempt to guide parents in their personal handling of the foregoing subject. I have no advice whatever for my minister friend and his wife, who themselves have never tasted a drop of beer, wine, or liquor, and who are confident that their four daughters will not do so either as long as they live. Whole volumes have been written on how to teach youngsters the other facts of life, but at least they do not involve, as this one does, any demonstrations conducted in the home. Perhaps some future disciple of the redoubtable Dr. Spock will contribute a detailed manual on exactly how to give a child its first drink.

Lacking such a guide, I at least can relate my own experience and those of many of my friends. Beer or wine has been on our dinner tables since our children first joined in our family meals. When as infants they wished to sample what the grown ups were drinking, they were allowed to taste it liberally diluted with water, and without any fuss. Usually they did not wish more. Both of my own adult sons learned by experience before they reached their teens that too much wine made them uncomfortably dizzy, just as they discovered that too much cake made them sick. They sometimes asked for a sip of someone's cocktail and found they did not like its flavor. They were told casually that liquor is stronger than wine or beer. As adults they cannot remember the first time they ever tasted any of these beverages. This last point may be significant, because a study of addictive drinkers has shown that almost without exception they remember in detail their first drink.

CHAPTER 16

Warnings of Danger

DURING THE YEARS I SPENT IN PREPARING TO WRITE THIS BOOK I interviewed some thousands of people in every section of the United States on the subject of drinks and drinking. Especially I attempted to learn what questions they might want such a volume to answer. They plied me with hundreds of miscellaneous queries, all of which are dealt with in various chapters. The oftenest-asked question was: "When am I in danger of becoming an alcoholic?"

To supply the information this calls for, it first would be well to discard the foggy term "alcoholic," which once was waggishly defined as "a friend you don't like who drinks as much as you do." What moderate users of alcoholic beverages really want to know is how to tell if they risk becoming "problem drinkers," an all-inclusive term that describes anyone who drinks enough and frequently enough to injure himself socially, economically, or physically.

(A "chronic alcoholic" is usually a person who suffers from the nutritional deficiency diseases caused by excessive drinking. A "habitual excessive drinker" can become a chronic alcoholic if he fails to balance his alcohol intake with a sufficiently nutritious diet and injures his system by repeated binges. An "addictive drinker" or "compulsive drinker" is a true addict who has lost control of his drinking; habitual excessive drinkers do not necessarily lose this control. Many chronic alcoholics are true addicts; some were epileptics, mentally deficient, or actively psychotic to begin with.)

The vast amount of fearsome publicity that accounts for the worry exhibited nowadays by millions of moderate drinkers is mostly focused on the chronic alcoholics, whose numbers, although not known exactly, are sufficiently great to represent a national problem.

Problem drinkers in general are people who, for any of several reasons not yet fully known to science, should never have taken even their first drink. They represent the 5 or 6 per cent of the drinking population—perhaps more; nobody knows—who are predisposed to become problem drinkers. The trouble is that most of them cannot be recognized as such until they have been drinking for several years.

Because of the number of years it takes for such people's drinking to reach the problem stage, early recognition of some danger signals is vital. Accordingly, the moderate drinkers who have asked that these signals be listed show their common sense in asking.

Simply put, you are in danger of becoming a problem drinker if (1) you find yourself gulping the first two or three drinks and drinking faster, much more, and oftener than others around you; or (2) you sneak drinks, take a couple of quick ones before going out, just in case there might not be enough at the party, or add a little extra to the shot glass when nobody is looking; or (3) you are disturbed if you cannot get a drink, and watch the clock until you can take it with a clear conscience; or (4) you find you now prefer to drink alone or only with strangers so that your friends will not know how much you are drinking; or (5) you begin experiencing "blackouts," losing your memory of the night before even though you did not "pass out."

If any of these symptoms characterize your drinking, you know that you are using alcoholic beverages to drug yourself rather than primarily for taste and pleasure, that your reaction to alcohol is abnormal and dangerous, that it has become a personality crutch, a way to dull anxiety, or to build confidence, or relieve boredom. There are the five early danger signals of problem drinking, the unmistakable signs that it is time to stop entirely.

At this stage there is still time, and plenty of help is available if you need it. If you find it is difficult to stop, or that you are uncomfortable without alcohol, see your family doctor, a psychiatrist, the nearest Alcoholism Information Center (fifty-eight cities have them), or join your local chapter of Alcoholics Anonymous.

But even without the danger signals, isn't the moderate social drinker taking a risk if he continues using alcoholic beverages regularly over a period of years? Hokum, say the researchers, who point out that millions have used alcohol steadily throughout their adult lives and have been healthy, solid, long-lived citizens of their communities. The risks of ordinary social drinking are solely those of dangerous behavior when one occasionally imbibes too much. It often has been contended that anyone who drinks too much long enough will become addicted to alcohol. Since no healthy, emotionally sound human beings have ever volunteered to subject themselves to an experiment to determine whether this might be true, the contention is without a shred of proof. If the highest estimates from impartially conducted surveys are accepted (they indicate four to five million problem drinkers in the United States), it is apparent that the person who sees none of the danger signals in himself need have no fear of becoming addicted.

There is a remaining often-asked question: "Is alcoholism really a disease?" It is argued heatedly between those who insist that compulsive drinking must be a disease because addicts cannot control it, and others who contend that problem drinkers are merely weak-kneed, spineless, spoiled brats. The researchers who first called alcohol addiction a disease have lately come to realize that the public thinks of a disease as something you can "catch"; and they now prefer to call it an "illness." Their scientific view is that a true compulsive drinker is the sickest, because he has lost control of his alcohol intake, and that a nonaddictive excessive drinker is at least psychologically or socially sick.

Finally, here is some advice for moderate drinkers about how *not* to treat a problem drinker. It is from an article distributed by the National Council on Alcoholism: Don't preach; don't have a holier-than-thou attitude; don't use the "if you loved me" appeal; don't hide his liquor or pour it out; don't argue with him when he is drunk; don't make an issue over his treatment; don't expect an immediate 100 per cent recovery; don't try to "protect" him against alcohol. And above all, don't persuade someone "on the wagon" to take a drink.

CHAPTER 17

A Plea for Sanity

THE SCHIZOPHRENIC ATTITUDE OF AMERICANS TOWARD DRINKS and drinking is the combined result of misinformation, fear, guilt feelings, and a set of federal, state, and local liquor laws as confused as a dipsomaniac's dreams. These strange laws and the regulations promulgated under their authority contribute as much to the misuse of alcoholic beverages as any of the other factors mentioned.

Of course, it is conceivable that on a legislative subject as clouded with mass emotion as this one, little improvement can be expected so long as (to quote a politician in one of the "dry" counties of Texas) "the wets have their liquor and the drys have their law." Nevertheless, a brief look at some of the ways our lawmakers have devised to control the demon rum may be of some interest.

The fifty United States have fifty different sets of liquor laws. The District of Columbia, by act of Congress, makes the number fifty-one, and contributes a novel provision that champagne may not be sold on Sunday, while it does not prohibit "sparkling wine," which means the same thing.

An airline stewardess, serving you a glass of wine twenty thousand feet over Iowa, unknowingly violates the law of that sovereign state until, minutes later, the jet plane crosses the Illinois line. A couple attending a tea dance in Virginia must take along their own liquor if they want any, and accordingly are inclined to kill the bottle before they leave the premises.

Neighboring Maryland, however, sees no harm in serving such people cocktails. At noon on a torrid New York Sunday a glass of cooling beer may not be purchased, but it becomes permissible at the moment the clock strikes one. In North Carolina you may have a glass of sherry brought to you by the waitress, but a bottle on your table is taboo. In Florida, Indiana, Kentucky, Massachusetts, and Wisconsin you must be seated to be served a drink, although California, New York, Pennsylvania, Illinois, and a number of other states have no objection if you prefer to take it standing up at the bar. Bars in North Dakota are forbidden to sell you anything to eat, but New York, Maine, New Hampshire, and some other states require all bars to serve food. Liquor stores in Oklahoma can sell you anything alcoholic, but are not allowed to deliver it to your home —a service that is supplied only by the state's bootleggers. Twenty-eight states prohibit the sale of liquor in food stores, but nine allow its sale almost anywhere, even in gas stations. New York liquor stores may sell you wine and spirits, but you must go to a grocery to buy a can of beer. A town in Wisconsin allows the sale of hard liquor, but prohibits the sale of beer.

In most of the seventeen "monopoly" states, liquor can be bought only in their state-operated stores, whose prophylactic *décor* would do credit to a neat police station. Rather than be seen entering one of these places, many a citizen of the State of Washington gets his wine from a food store, which buys it at retail from the neighboring state store and adds a further markup. Most of the state monopolies indirectly discourage people from buying wines in their stores, because hard liquor pours the most net profit into the public till.

We also still have the archaic laws forbidding the sale of anything alcoholic while the polls are open on election days. This causes leading restaurants to serve drinks in cups to their favored customers, and makes the exempt bar at the United Nations Building the most popular place in New York City until the voting booths are closed. In Sacramento, California, an assembly district special election resulted in the north side of the city's main street being legally "dry" all day while bartenders on the south side of the street did double their usual business.

Young people in most states eagerly await their twenty-first birthdays, which by law qualify them as adults to buy liquor legally. Bartenders and store owners, in order to protect their licenses, insist on scanning their youthful customers' drivers' licenses or birth certificates, which often are forged or borrowed. In New York State, however, youths become eligible for this adult status symbol at only eighteen, a fact that brings nightly streams of youngsters from neighboring New Jersey and Connecticut to patronize the Empire State's stores and bars. In Illinois and North Dakota, girls may drink at eighteen, but young men not until they are twenty-one. North Carolina considers a married person of seventeen old enough, while a thirsty unmarried person must be twenty-one. Wisconsin allows a girl of eighteen accompanied by her parent or guardian to drink, but if she is with her husband she may not, because according to a court decision, a husband is not his wife's guardian.

New York's Legislature is continually bombarded with demands from neighboring states that its eighteen-year age minimum be raised to twenty-one. Pointing out that the present law has stood since 1886, prior to which the age was sixteen, and even earlier fourteen, New York still refuses to change. The city of Washington with its eighteen-year minimum is another oasis for thirsty young people, who travel from distant points in Maryland and Virginia to stock up in the nation's capital.

Strangest of all is the situation in Mississippi, the last remaining member of the Union with a statewide prohibition law. The sale of liquor in Mississippi is, if anything, conducted more openly than in many a legally "wet" state. An incredible height of hypocrisy is reached by the Mississippi law that collects a tax on all spirits and wine that are brought illegally into the state. A Mississippi official goes to a liquor house in neighboring Louisiana to levy the tax. Before sheriffs of Mississippi counties will allow sale of the imported contraband, they require proof that the Louisiana shipper has paid the Mississippi Treasury the black-market tax. The "dry" state's tax collector gets a copy of each wholesale sales invoice when a Mississippi dealer makes his purchase in Louisiana.

Mississippi is littered with "lounges," a euphemism for its saloons. Even tea rooms urge their patrons to take cocktails with meals, including breakfast. Published federal records show that more than three thousand Mississippi dealers pay their annual fee for occupational tax stamps, which qualify them, as far as the United States Government is concerned, to sell beer and wine. Nobody was in the least surprised when a study by the University of Mississippi showed that more than a million gallons of federally tax-paid wine and liquor were shipped into the state in a single year. It is generally predicted, however, that Mississippi will remain legally dry as long as the last voter can stagger to the polls.

Every state taxes 80- and 90-proof distilled liquors exactly the same as 100-proof, which means that the consumer pays a liquor tax on the extra water with which the low-proof spirits are diluted.

All of the peculiar state laws are devised in the name of public morals, safety, and welfare, and therefore presumably have some moral basis. This means, then, that what is moral behavior in many states is immoral in certain others. The contortions of Nevada's legislative conscience in permitting gambling are no more astounding than those of the other forty-nine states in regulating liquor.

In addition to the strange situations already mentioned, there are the "drip-dry" states, in which some towns and counties have prohibition while neighboring communities are "wet." In 1959, 67 per cent of the people of Tennessee were living in "dry" areas, 62 per cent of those in Georgia, 58 per cent in North Carolina, 49 per cent in Alabama, and 44 per cent of those in Kansas. Eighty-seven of the 120 counties in Kentucky, which has more distilleries than any other state, are legally "dry."

Each year the perennial seesaw battle between wets and drys is refought in hundreds of local elections in about two dozen of the states, some of which have laws requiring "wet" communities to vote on the issue every two years. There were 443 elections in 1957 and 1,488 in 1958. The drys have been losing ground slowly. In 1947 almost one in five Americans lived in a locality where alcoholic beverages could not be purchased legally. By 1959, following the repeal of Oklahoma's fifty-two-year-old prohibition law, the number was down to one in seven.

Yet there is no town in the United States (or in Canada, which has "drip-dry" localities, too) where a drink cannot be bought at any time of the day or night, although it may be in a "club" or speakeasy.

This might be expected to dismay the dry forces, but exactly the opposite is true. To understand the prohibitionists requires a few key facts and some cogitation. Their amateur ranks are the maidenly ladies of the W.C.T.U. and scattered fanatics who feed emotionally on anything they can find to hate, or who are working off their shame for having had drunken fathers. (Carry Nation, who in 1899 smashed countless saloons with her hatchet, was originally married to a sot.) But the hard core of professional drys are in a business with a lucrative source of income in the tax-free contributions they solicit through thousands of churches. Some of their visiting clergymen who deliver Bible-thumping guest sermons against John Barleycorn, giving the local minister the Sunday off, have been known to spurn the coins that clink on the collection plate, preferring to get pledges from wealthy members of the flock, whom they later solicit personally for far more substantial contributions.

The demon rum is the professional prohibitionists' drum, which they will continue kicking as long as it will make noise. And nothing provides as favorable opportunities to kick it as loudly as the continuous local wet-dry election fights.

Legislators, the great majority of whom are personally liberal in their own drinking, get the drumbeats from the drys' letter-writing brigades, small groups of people who fill the mail with floods of form letters that make the number of prohibitionists seem vast. Much of the existing restrictive, confusing, unenforceable liquor legislation represents the lawmakers' bowing down to a vociferous minority element that in some states just barely exists.

In latter years the dry professionals, recognizing that in some localities their old-fashioned cries of doom no longer were registering with prospective contributors, have changed their propaganda line. In what Bergen Birdsall, executive secretary of the California Temperance Federation (successor to that state's Anti-Saloon League) calls "a rear-guard action," they now preach "alcohol education" and "local control" or "community veto." The latter is their euphemism for local prohibition, which when enacted by a town or county sends its residents to adjoining "wet" areas to do their tippling, following which, in their alcoholized condition, they must drive home. And to make their legislative programs more palatable, some dry groups are even abandoning the word "temperance." (The former Washington State Temperance Association is now the Washington Alcohol Problems Association.)

The early history of drinking among the Protestant clergy sheds some light on the prohibition movement. Until the late eighteenth century, heavy drinking by ministers was so common that it presented a serious problem. Pastors visiting the homes of their parishioners were expected to imbibe at every stop they made, and did, to a scandalous degree. The reaction against their excesses began in England, with a campaign to reduce ministerial drinking. The campaign did not stop with the clergy; it eventually became the national prohibition movement. Pastors spread word that drunkards' breath near a candle flame often caught fire, that drinkers' blood boiled in their veins by spontaneous combustion, that many topers were exploding like kegs of dynamite, and that women who drank while pregnant gave birth to monsters. In church after church, it became impossible to drink anything alcoholic and still be considered a Christian.

In recent years the pendulum has begun to swing the other way. Methodist Bishop John Wesley Lord in 1959, while still standing four square for total abstinence, proposed that until prohibition can return, the liquor industry should be nationalized. In the same year the Episcopal Church, never noted for abstemiousness on the part of its members, became more liberal than before. A report of its Joint Commission on Alcoholism made it clear, in the words of Bishop J. Brooke Mosley, that Episcopalians "under well-defined conditions . . . can drink to the Glory of God."

The Catholic Church, meanwhile, has stood fast against intemperate legislation as well as intemperate drinking. "Our laws," says Monsignor J. D. Conway, president of the Canon Law Society of America, "should not be inspired by crusading bottle smashers, but by wise and tolerant students of social problems, who are not scandalized that a man takes a drink, but who are sensible of the evils of excess."

Any "wise and tolerant" view of the liquor laws and regulations in the United States readily discloses that they are a crazy quilt of conflicting restrictions that treat any use of alcoholic beverages as a legally tolerated sin, keep alive mass feelings of guilt, and perpetuate the billion-dollar-a-year moonshine industry.

If the various chapters of this volume convey any basic facts, they are: (1) that drinking has been a normal part of human behavior since prehistoric times; (2) that the more diluted beverages are preferable to the stronger ones, from the standpoints of the individual and of society; (3) that their use is most temperate when it accompanies family meals; (4) that anything which tends to maintain the bootleg traffic helps to support organized crime; and (5) finally, as the next chapter will show, that excessive drinking is rarest in those groups where moderate drinking is part of their cultural pattern, where to drink or not to drink is not an issue—where it is a matter of no importance.

CHAPTER 18

Manners for Drinking America

THE CIVILIZING PROCESS OF THE BRUTE HUMAN, LONG STUDIED by savants and philosophers, includes in its advanced stages the development of the connoisseur spirit, selectivity among the things we do, consideration for one's fellow man, and the acquisition of good manners.

Drinking customs go through a similar process, which in twentieth-century America is still occurring. Some progress toward civilized drinking, although far from uniform at all social strata, is beginning to show in certain quarters.

Whether some of the recent marked changes in liquor-use patterns represent progress is, of course, debatable. Some of them arouse alarm among people who fear all alcohol. Instead of the pre-prohibition saloon that self-respecting females dared not enter, there is the cocktail lounge where stately matrons sit at the bar and name their favorite brands of liquor. The bathtub gin of the "dry" 1920's is almost forgotten, but some of the same people who once consumed it still lap up three Martinis each night before dinner. Numerous ladies' bridge clubs, successors to the sewing circles of an earlier generation, are serving beverages considerably stronger than tea. Women's magazines which once refused liquor ads now publish them regularly, including those that picture "The Lady of Distinction."

Some other changes may be more significant. In 1956 a Gallup poll showed that 46 per cent of American women abstained from drinking any alcoholic beverage. In 1958 a similar poll showed 55 per cent abstaining. Perhaps this has something to do with Eleanor Roosevelt's widely quoted comment that "women are, if anything, more unattractive than men when they have had too much to drink."

Women are taking greater control of their households, including what was once solely a man's prerogative—the buying and serving of beer, wine, and liquor. They also have control of the money; nearly two thirds of all savings accounts are in their names; millions of women are employed, earning billions of dollars yearly; thousands are holding public office; almost a million are in business management. Result: the influence of husbands is declining.

This growing feminine power alone can bring about major developments in social behavior. Actually both sexes are involved in what is happening.

There are signs that the appeal of cocktail parties is beginning to wear thin. While this American-born custom continues to spread abroad (even England's Queen Elizabeth II holds them now in Buckingham Palace), the dull sameness of virtually all such affairs causes many bored guests to avoid them. Business firms are beginning to wonder whether they need to serve liquor each time they invite customers to witness some presentation.

People with increasing leisure are engaging in hobbies and outdoor activities that compete with heavy weekend drinking. Touring Americans and servicemen return from abroad with newly educated tastes for wines and gourmet cookery.

The falling-down drunk, once taken for granted, is becoming virtually extinct. The nation's bars, still dimly lit during the 1940's, are turning on brighter lights as their patrons' behavior improves and as their visits become less furtive. People who become ill in public from drinking too much are now regarded as disgraced. The prohibition custom of toting a hip flask to a football game seems finally to be dying out. And the man who strives to be kingpin of the party by proving he can hold more liquor than anyone else finds that the host does not invite him again.

These things bring into focus a potent influence on all human behavior. Sociologists call it a "cultural pattern." Schoolteachers score it as "deportment." To the rest of us it is acceptable conduct, social conformity, or, more plainly, good manners.

Scientists seeking the causes of inebriety have become inquisitive about cultural patterns. Primitive cultures, in particular, are proving so interesting that a search has been launched among the world's remaining aborigines for additional light on alcoholic behavior. University of California sociologist Edwin Lemert, on a mission for the National Institute of Mental Health, lived for months among the Indian tribes of British Columbia, then among the island natives of Polynesia, to study their drinking customs. This is what he learned: "Where there is drunkenness without civilization, there has not been the problem of alcoholism."

In most primitive tribes, it appears, the people gather to drink together, usually in religious rites. They imbibe purposely to become frenzied and continue until they sink into stupor. But when they recover, it is taboo to drink anything alcoholic again until the next tribal drinking occasion. Those who violate tribal taboos are ostracized and driven away.

Studies of ethnic, racial, and religious groups in civilized countries are also supplying some significant clues.

It is noted that in Scandinavia, where drinking by women is frowned upon, males outnumber females among chronic alcoholics by 23 to 1, compared to the 5-to-1 ratio in the United States and the 1.5-to-1 ratio in England. In India, says Rajendra Singh, a member of the Indian Parliament, "a man who drinks excessively is looked down upon as being of an unsound mind."

The lowest incidence of addictive drinking found in any single group in the United States is among people of the Jewish faith. The highest rate is among Americans of Irish origin. Sociologists, studying these population segments intensively, find that virtually all Jews use alcoholic beverages, as their religion has required for thousands of years, and that the few who become problem drinkers are those who have drifted away from their cultural group. A survey of orthodox Jewish college students shows that at least half of them exhibit "disgust, intolerance, scorn, and loss of respect" to drunkenness among other men. On the other hand, the investigators find that among the Irish, hard drinking by adults is mainly taken for granted.

For more than a generation the pattern of American post-prohibition drinking has been mirrored more or less accurately in the press, where stories of drunken antics have been treated with tolerant humor and blasé accounts of holiday season festivities have implied that normal citizens always have hangovers on New Year's Day.

Behavior standards in America are enforced, even as are those in primitive tribes, by ostracism of those who violate cultural taboos. People who pick their noses or their teeth in public, or who merely eat their food from their knives, are currently barred from polite society.

When enough Americans become equally intolerant of common drunkenness, there will be fewer excessive drinkers.

APPENDIX

Guide to Wines, Spirits, and Drink Terms

This appendix contains explanations of only those beverages and drink terms not defined in the preceding chapters. For references to terms not listed in this Guide, see the Index.

Advokaat (ahd-vo-kaht)—An egg-and-brandy liqueur, similar to eggnog; 40-proof.

Aguardiente—Spanish term for all distilled spirits; literally, "ardent water."

Alcohol—Usually refers to ethyl (beverage) alcohol. Pure (200-proof) alcohol is usually synthetic and is used only for laboratory purposes. Almost-pure (190-proof) alcohol, usually labeled "grain neutral spirits" is sold in liquor stores, as freely as whiskey, gin, etc., in the following states: Alaska, Arkansas, Colorado, Connecticut, Florida, Georgia, Illinois, Kansas, Kentucky, Maryland, Missouri, Nebraska, Nevada, North Carolina, North Dakota, New Jersey, New Mexico, Oklahoma, Pennsylvania, South Carolina, South Dakota, Tennessee, Texas, Utah, Virginia, West Virginia, Wyoming, and in the District of Columbia. Other states require purchasers, such as doctors and druggists, to obtain special permits.

Amer—A bitter apéritif made of wine and brandy with added flavorings, used in mixed drinks or drunk diluted with soda, sometimes sweetened with grenadine; 78 proof. The original product made in France is Amer Picon, a proprietary name.

Amontillado (ah-mon-tee-*ya*-do)—A type of Spanish sherry, usually dry, sometimes slightly sweet.

Angelica—Sweet white dessert wine.

Anisette—Colorless liqueurs flavored with anise seed; they come at various strengths, from 48- to 92-proof. There also are dry anise liquors, such as the 92-proof Greek product called Ouzo.

Apéritif (ah-pay-re-teef)—*see* "Dessert" wines.

Appellation Contrôlée—This term on a French wine label is a claim that the wine was grown in the delimited viticultural district whose name it bears, from approved grape varieties only, and according to the locally recognized method of vinification.

"Appetizer" wines—*see* "Dessert" wines.

Apple wine—*see* Cider.

Apricot Liqueur—Apricot-flavored liqueur with a brandy base, usually 60- to 80-proof. Some makers call theirs by proprietary names, such as Abricotine and Abry. There also are apricot-flavored brandies, usually 70-proof.

Aroma—*see* Bouquet.

Asti Spumante—Italian white sparkling wine, like champagne, but with a spicy Muscat grape flavor; usually medium-sweet.

Auslese (ows-lay-zeh)—A term on German wine labels, by which the vintner claims the grapes were fully ripe and carefully selected.

Beerenauslese means that each individual grape was carefully selected as perfectly ripe.

Spätlese means the grapes were left on the vine to become partly raisined and to grow the "noble mold."

Trockenbeerenauslese means the grapes were almost completely raisined; wines so labeled are very sweet and enormously expensive.

Balthazar—Large wine bottle, equivalent to 16 regular-size bottles.

B & B Liqueur—Mixture of brandy and Benedictine, 86-proof.

Banyuls—A sweet appetizer wine produced near Banyuls in France.

Barbera (bar-*bay*-ra)—Dry, tart red table wine of the Barbera grape.

Barberone—Dry, tart red table wine.

Barolo—Italian dry, tart red table wine.

Barsac—A French sweet white table wine, similar to sweet sauterne.

Beaujolais (bo-zho-lay)—A French dry red burgundy.

Beer Strengths by States—These are the maximum strengths, in per cent of alcohol by volume, permitted for any malt beverages in the following states: Massachusetts, 15%. North Carolina, 6¼%. Arkansas, South Carolina, Tennessee, Wisconsin, 6¼%, but higher strengths permitted when dealers pay higher license fees. Georgia, 6%. Louisiana, New Hampshire, Vermont, 6%, but higher strengths permitted in Louisiana on payment of higher license fees, and in New Hampshire and Vermont when sold in state-operated stores. Maximum in dry areas of Louisiana, 4%. Alabama, Idaho, Iowa, Montana, Washington, 5%, but higher strengths permitted for state-operated stores. Mississippi, 5%. North Dakota, Texas, 5%, but higher strengths permitted if dealers pay higher licenses. California and Oregon prohibit beverages labeled "beer" from exceeding 5% by volume, but Oregon allows "ale" or "malt liquor" to be as high as 10%, while California has no such maximum. South Dakota, 7½%, except "non-intoxicating" beer, 4%. Kansas, Oklahoma, Utah, and West Virginia, 4%, but higher strengths permitted for Kansas and Oklahoma liquor stores and for Utah and West Virginia state-operated stores. Colorado, 4% for "beer," but no maximum for "malt liquor." Florida and Virginia, 4% for dry areas, no limit elsewhere. Minnesota charges higher license fees and taxes for malt beverages over 4%. Missouri and Ohio have a 4% maximum for "beer," but "malt liquor" may be as high as 6¼% in Missouri and 8¾% in Ohio. Illinois and Kentucky allow local elections to set maximums of 5% and 4% by volume, respectively, but have no other limits. No maximum limit in Alaska, Arizona, Connecticut, Delaware, Hawaii, Indiana, Maine, Maryland, Michigan, Nebraska, New Jersey, New Mexico, New York, Pennsylvania, Rhode Island, Wyoming or District of Columbia, except that Maryland's Harford County has a 6% limit. Nevada has a 5% by volume minimum, and no maximum limit.

Beerenauslese—*see Auslese.*

Benedictine—A golden, spicy liqueur with an angelica oil base, containing dozens of herbs, spices, and seeds, honey, and brandy; 86-proof. The name is a French proprietary, but there are many less expensive equivalents, whose names generally begin with "B."

Black Muscat—Spicy red dessert wine of the Black Muscat grape.

"Body"—The substance, consistency, fullness, and richness of a beverage, resulting from the solid matter dissolved or suspended in the liquid.

Bordeaux Blanc—French white table wine, dry or slightly sweet.

Bordeaux Rouge—French dry, tart red table wine.

"Bottled at the Winery"—This term on a wine label means much the same as "Produced."

Bouquet—Refers to the winy perfume of an aged wine, as distinguished from "aroma," which is that part of the fragrance of wine originating from the grapes used.

Branch water—A term used in the South for cold water added to liquor; literally, the water of a small stream.

"Bulk Process"—A term the United States Government requires to appear on a champagne label if the secondary fermentation that gives the wine its sparkle is carried on in a container larger than one gallon. Also called the Charmat process. "Bulk process" champagnes are usually less expensive than their "bottle-fermented" counterparts.

Burgundy—Red table wine, dry and tart or slightly sweet and soft. There also are white burgundies, which are always dry.

Cabernet Sauvignon (cab-er-nay so-veen-yohn)—Dry, tart red table wine of the Cabernet Sauvignon grape.

Campari—Italian red bitters, like a bitter vermouth, used in highballs and in such cocktails as the negroni, 48-proof. This is a proprietary name, but there are similarly named American counterparts.

Caramel—Burnt sugar, slightly bitter but otherwise tasteless, used to color brandies, rums, and blended whiskeys.

Chablis (shah-blee)—Dry white table wine.

Champagne—White sparkling wine, dry, medium-sweet, or sweet. There also are pink champagnes and red champagnes. "American," "New York State," "Ohio" Champagnes are likely to have some "foxy" flavor. *See* also "Bulk Process."

Charbono—Dry, tart red table wine of the Charbono grape.

"Charcoal Mellowed"—On a whiskey label, this term means the liquor has been filtered through charcoal to smooth its taste. A government ruling limits the amount of charcoal used. Whiskeys that are heavily treated are no longer eligible to be called "bourbon" or "rye."

Chardonnay—Chablis of the Pinot Chardonnay grape.

Charmat—*see* Bulk Process.

Chassagne—A French white burgundy.

Chartreuse (shar-truz)—A French liqueur said to contain 130 herbs and spices in its secret formula. Green Chartreuse is 110-proof, yellow Chartreuse is 86-proof.

"Château" sauterne—Sweet sauterne.

Châteauneuf-du-Pape (sha-toe-nuf-du-pap)—A dry, tart red wine from the Rhône Valley of France.

Chemise—*see* Sediment.

Chenin Blanc (sheh-nan blahnk)—Sweet white table wine of the Chenin blanc grape.

Cherry Liqueur—A number of cherry-colored liqueurs with cherry flavor and a sweetened brandy base, 49- to 60-proof, the most famous of which is Denmark's Cherry Heering. Not to be confused with the colorless cherry brandy known as kirsch or kirschwasser, or with cherry-flavored brandies, usually 70-proof.

Chianti (kee-*ahn*-tee)—Dry, tart red table wine, usually sold in straw-covered bottles. There also are some white chiantis.

Cider—In the United States, means unfermented apple juice. "Hard cider" is fermented cider, usually 7 to 11% in alcoholic content. In other countries cider (also spelled *cyder* and *cidre*) means the fermented product. Legally, homemade hard cider must not exceed 7% in alcoholic content. In Colonial days cider was usually drunk with added raisins, other flavorings, and sugar. When apple brandy is added to hard cider, it is called apple wine, which usually is 20% in alcohol content.

Claret—Dry, tart red table wine, usually lighter-bodied than burgundy.

Clos de Vougeot (clo-deh-voo-zho)—A French red burgundy.

Cobblers—Tall sweet drinks of wine or liquor with fruits and plenty of ice.

Cocktail sherry—Slightly sweet sherry.

Coffee liqueurs—Usually 53- to 60-proof. Examples are Kahlua and Tia Maria.

Cointreau Liqueur (kwan-tro)—A colorless, sweet orange-peel liqueur, called Triple Sec by other makers; 80-proof. The Cointreau name is proprietary, and is used on other liqueurs as well.

Collins—Tall drinks containing liquor, lemon or lime, sugar, and soda.

Cologne spirits—Neutral spirits.

Crackling wines—Sparkling wines that sparkle only faintly. Also called *pétillant* (French) and *frizzante* (Italian).

Cream sherry—sweet sherry.

Crème d'Ananas—Pineapple liqueur.

Crème de Bananes—Banana liqueur, 56-proof.

Crema de Chocolate—Chocolate liqueur, 52-proof.

Crème de Cacao—A white or brown liqueur, 50- to 60-proof, flavored with cacao and vanilla beans, base of the Alexander cocktail.

Crème de Cassis—A liqueur flavored with black currants; 35- to 50-proof.

Crème de Fraises—Strawberry liqueur.

Crème de Framboises—Raspberry liqueur.

Crème de Mandarine—Liqueur flavored with dried peel of tangerine oranges; 60-proof.

Crème de Menthe—A white, green, or gold liqueur flavored with oil of mint leaves; 60-proof; used with brandy to make the stinger cocktail.

Crème de Noyaux (no-yo)—Almond-tasting liqueur made from crushed seeds of apricots, cherries, peaches, and plums, with orange-peel flavoring and a brandy base; 60-proof.

Crème de Rose—Liqueur flavored with rose petals and vanilla.

Crème de Vanille—Vanilla-flavored liqueur.

Crème de Violette—Liqueur flavored with violets and vanilla.

Crème Yvette—A violet-flavored, blue- or violet-colored liqueur.

Cups—Wine drinks, similar to punches, made with fruits and liqueurs.

Cru—Leading vineyards of Bordeaux in France were classified in 1855 as producing first, second, third, fourth, or fifth *crus* (growths). The term has little meaning, however, because many a third or fourth *cru* is conceded to be superior to many a first or second *cru.*

Crust—*see* Sediment.

Curaçao (cure-ah-so)—Yellowish orange-colored, green, or blue, or colorless, strongly flavored orange-peel liqueur, 60-proof, compared to the 80-proof, colorless Cointreau and Triple Sec liqueurs, which it otherwise resembles.

Dash—1/6 teaspoon or 1/48 fluid ounce.

Decanting—The act of gently pouring wine from its original bottle, in which it has deposited sediment, into a new container; often performed by the light of a candle flame.

Delaware—White table wine of the Delaware grape, with "foxy" flavor; dry to medium-sweet.

Demijohn—Wicker-covered large wine bottle, usually 4.9 gallons.

"Dessert" wines—In the United States, this term includes all wines containing more than 14 per cent and not over 21 per cent alcohol. Most of them are sweet, but the "dessert" class also includes the "appetizer" wines, which are the sherries, madeiras, marsalas, and the apéritifs, such as the vermouths and the new flavored wines.

D.O.M.—Part of the trade mark of Benedictine Liqueur. The letters stand for *Deo Optimo Maximo* ("To God, most good, most great").

Drambuie—A golden liqueur with a Scotch malt whiskey base, flavored with spices and honey; 80-proof.

Enology—The study of wines; from *oinos,* Greek for wine.

"Estate-bottled"—On a wine label means that 100 per cent of the grapes were grown in the winery owner's vineyard and that all of the wine in the bottle was made in his own adjoining cellar.

Falernum—A colorless spiced syrup, slightly alcoholic, used in flavoring rum drinks.

Fermentation—The changing of sugars, by the action of yeast, into ethyl alcohol and carbon dioxide; the process by which grains and fruits become beer and wine.

"Fifth"—Four-fifth quart bottle; 25.6 fluid ounces; 1/5 gallon.

Fino (fee-no)—A type of Spanish sherry, dry and "nutty" with characteristic *flor* flavor.

Fiori Alpini—An Italian yellow liqueur, 92-proof, sold in tall bottles with rock-sugar crystals inside in the shape of a tree.

Fizzes—Effervescent tall drinks, traditionally intended as morning hangover cures, made with various liquors and wines, fruit juices, syrups, sugar, soda, and sometimes with added egg white (for silver fizz) or yolk (for golden fizz).

Flavored brandies—Neutral grape brandies flavored with apricot, blackberry, cherry, ginger, peach, raspberry, and other fruits; usually 70-proof and sweet. In other countries these products are called "blackberry brandy," "cherry brandy," etc., but U.S. regulations prohibit such labels unless the brandy is distilled from the fruit named. If they are less than 70-proof, they are called liqueurs or cordials.

Flips—Drinks made with egg or egg yolk, various wines and liquors, sugar, and cracked ice.

Flor—see "Nutty."

Forbidden Fruit—A citrus liqueur.

"Fortified"—A term formerly used to designate dessert wines, to which brandy is added during fermentation to check action of the yeasts and to keep the wines sweet. Use of this word to designate any wine is now prohibited by U.S. regulations.

"Foxy"—Refers to the grape flavor you get in most bottled and canned grape juice. It is the fragrant personality of the Concord grape variety and its many relatives among domesticated native American grapevines.

French-type vermouth—Dry vermouth.

Frizzante—see Crackling wines.

Galliano—A yellow Italian liqueur, 80-proof.

Gallon—The U.S. gallon is 128 fluid ounces. The British or "imperial" gallon is 1.2 U.S. gallons.

Gamay—Red burgundy of the Gamay grape.

Gevrey-Chambertin (zhevray-sham-bair-tan)—A French red burgundy.

Gewürz Traminer (geh-wurtz trah-mee-ner)—Spicy white table wine of the Gewürztraminer grape, dry or medium-sweet.

Glögg—A Scandinavian hot spiced drink similar to mulled wine, but with added aquavit or other spirit.

Goldwasser—A citrus-flavored, spicy liqueur containing flecks of genuine, harmless gold leaf; also called Liqueur d'Or. It owes its origin to the early belief that gold could cure diseases.

Grand Marnier—A French Curaçao liqueur, 80-proof, with a cognac base.

Graves (grahv)—A French white table wine, dry or medium-sweet. There also are some red Graves wines.

Green Hungarian—White table wine of the Green Hungarian grape, usually dry.

Grenache (gren-*ahsh*)—*see* Rosé.

Grenadine—Nonalcoholic syrup of pomegranates or red currants, used as a flavoring. There also are grenadine liqueurs.

Grey Riesling—Dry white table wine of the Grey Riesling grape.

Grignolino (green-yo-*lee*-no)—Dry, soft red or pink table wine of the Grignolino grape.

Grog—The rum ration, a mixture of one third rum and two thirds water, that is issued to crews of British and Canadian naval vessels at eleven o'clock each morning when the bos'n pipes "up spirits." On some Canadian ships it is now permissible to substitute cola for the water. A heavy-bodied rum is used. Men who decline the grog ration receive, as the wages of virtue, a money allowance instead.

Half and Half—In the U.S., a bottled blend of port and sherry. In England, a popular drink made of equal parts of ale and stout.

Haut sauterne (oh so-tairn)—Medium-sweet or sweet sauterne.

Hermitage (air-me-taj)—Dry red or white table wine from the Rhône Valley of France.

Hock—Refers to Rhine wine.

Hoochinoo—An alcoholic drink made clandestinely by Alaskan Indians of the Hutsnuwu tribe, from boiled fern and flour. Later, American soldiers added molasses and distilled it. This is the origin of the slang term "hooch" for illicit liquor.

Irish Coffee—Strong black coffee, sugar, and Irish whiskey, with a float of chilled whipped cream.

Irish Mist—A liqueur with an Irish whiskey base, 80-proof.

Italian-type vermouth—Sweet vermouth.

Jeroboam—Large wine bottle, equivalent to 4 regular-size bottles.

Jigger—1½ fluid ounce.

Johannisberger Riesling—Rhine wine of the Johannisberger (White) Riesling grape; dry or medium-sweet.

Kahlua—*see* Coffee Liqueur.

Kümmel (kim-mel)—Colorless liqueur flavored with caraway and other seeds, 80-proof.

Lacrima Christi—Italian white table wine, dry or medium-sweet. There also is a sparkling version. The name means "Tears of Christ."

Liebfraumilch (leeb-frow-milsh)—Various inexpensive German rhine wines, dry or medium-sweet. The name means "Milk of the Blessed Virgin."

Light beer—Means, in Canada, beer containing less than 2½% alcohol by volume. It is sold in Newfoundland and Prince Edward Island provinces.

Light Muscat—Spicy white table wine of the Muscat grape, dry or sweet.

"Liqueur Scotch," "Liqueur Brandy"—A term used on labels to imply that the spirits are old and smooth enough to be sipped straight, in the manner of liqueurs.

Liqueur d'Or—*see* Goldwasser.

Mâcon (ma-cohn)—A French red burgundy.

Madeira (ma-*day*-ra)—A sherry-type wine that ranges from dry to sweet.

Magnum—Large wine bottle, equivalent to two regular-size (fifth) bottles.

Malaga—American foxy-flavored sweet red table wine. Spanish Malaga is a dessert wine.

Malvasia Bianca—Spicy white table wine of the Malvasia bianca grape; dry or sweet.

Manzanilla (mahn-za-nee-ya)—A light type of Spanish sherry.

Maraschino Liqueur—A colorless liqueur of marasca cherries, flavored with rose petals and spices; 60- and 64-proof. It is used mainly to flavor cocktails and fruit dishes.

Margaux (mar-go)—A French dry, tart red table wine.

Marsala (mar-*sah-la*)—A sherry-type wine that ranges from dry to sweet.

Masticha—A Greek liqueur, 92-proof.

Mavrodaphne—A Greek red sweet dessert wine, similar to port.

May wine—Sweet white table wine flavored with woodruff.

Médoc (may-doc)—French dry, tart red table wine.

Metaxa—A dark, sweet, resinous Greek liqueur with a brandy base, 92-proof.

Methusaleh—Large wine bottle, equivalent to 8 regular-size bottles.

Meursault (mere-soh)—A French white burgundy.

Mezcal—A Mexican liquor, stronger in flavor than tequila. Like tequila, it is distilled from the fermented juice of the maguey cactus. The kind from Oaxaca traditionally has an inch-long maguey worm floating in each bottle as evidence that the liquor is genuine. This is the same worm that is fried and eaten in Mexico and regarded as a great delicacy.

Mise en bouteille au château—This term (or *mise du château*) on a French wine label means the wine was bottled at the winery where it was made.

Montilla (mon-*tee*-ya)—A dry, bitter type of Spanish sherry.

Montrachet (mohn-ra-shay)—A French white burgundy.

Moselle—White table wine, dry or medium-sweet.

Mousseux—*see* Sparkling wines.

Mulled wine—Hot spiced wine.

Muscatel—Spicy sweet white dessert wine of the Muscat grape.

Muscat Frontignan (fron-teen-yon)—Muscatel of the Muscat Frontignan (Muscat Canelli) grape.

Nebbiolo—Italian dry, tart red table wine.

Nebuchadnezzar—Large wine bottle, equivalent to 20 regular-size bottles.

Neuchâtel—Swiss dry, tart white table wine.

Niagara—White table wine of the Niagara grape, "foxy" flavored.

Niersteiner—A German rhine wine, dry or medium-sweet.

"Noble mold"—The *botrytis cinerea* mold; the French call it *pourriture noble*. It grows on grapes that are left to become partly raisined on the vine, and gives some French sauternes and German *Spätlese* rhine wines their distinctive flavor.

Nuits Saint-Georges (nwee san-zhorz)—French red burgundy.

"Nutty"—Refers to the characteristic oxidized or *rancio* flavor of sherry, madeira, and marsala wines. The Spanish fino and a few of the California sherries have a distinctly different *rancio* taste, produced by a film yeast that grows on the wine's surface in a partially filled cask. These are called *flor* sherries, but that word rarely appears on a label.

O.F.C.—Old Fine Canadian.

Oloroso—A type of Spanish sherry, slightly sweet or sweet.

Originalabfüllung—German label term for bottled at the winery. *Originalabzug* and *Wachstum* have similar meaning.

Orvieto—Italian white table wine, usually dry.

Ouzo—*see* Anisette.

Peppermint Schnapps—Mint-flavored liqueur, lighter-bodied than Crème de Menthe; 60-proof.

Pernod—Best-known of the several proprietary-named, anise-flavored substitutes for absinthe; 90- and 100-proof.

Perry—Pear wine.

Pétillant—*see* Crackling wines.

Piesporter—A German rhine wine, dry or medium-sweet.

Pinot Blanc (pee-no blahnk)—Chablis of the Pinot Blanc grape.

Pinot Noir (pee-no nwar)—Red burgundy of the Pinot Noir grape.

Pomerol—French dry, tart red table wine.

Pommard (Po-mar)—French red burgundy.

Pony—1 fluid ounce. Also, an eighth-barrel (3⅞ gallons) beer keg.

Port—Sweet red dessert wine. Ruby port is sometimes sweeter than the "regular," tawny port is sometimes a little less sweet. "American," "New York State," and "Ohio" ports are likely to have some "foxy" flavor. There also are white ports.

Pot still—The old-fashioned pot-bellied still in which a fermented mash or wine is boiled and the vapor captured and condensed as spirit. "Pot still" whiskey is made in this type of still.

Pouilly-Fuissé (pwee-yee-fwee-say)—French white burgundy.

Pousse-Café—A glass of six different-colored liqueurs, poured slowly in layers, the lighter ones floating on those that are heavier.

"Produced"—This term on a wine label means the vintner crushed, fermented, and matured at least 75 per cent of the wine in the bottle.

Prunelle—A brown plum liqueur.

Punch—Any drink of many ingredients; its name is derived from Hindustani and Sanskrit words meaning five.

Quetsch (ketch)—A colorless prune brandy.

Raki—A colorless, harsh, unaged Middle Eastern spirit, distilled from wine and fruits or their residue, usually with added flavorings.

Red Pinot (pee-no)—Dry, tart red table wine of the Red Pinot grape.

Rehoboam—Large wine bottle, equivalent to 6 regular-size bottles.

Retsina (ret-*see*-na)—Greek wine flavored with resin.

Rhine wine—White table wine. California rhine wines are dry; those of other states and those of Germany are dry or medium-sweet.

Rickeys—Various drinks made with spirits or liqueurs, lime or lemon, sweetening, and soda or ginger ale.

Riesling (rees-ling)—White table wine of White Riesling, Grey Riesling, or Sylvaner grapes; dry or medium-sweet.

Rioja (ree-oh-ha)—Spanish dry, tart red table wine.

Rock and Rye—Light-amber liqueur made of rye whiskey, neutral spirits, and rock candy syrup, usually with pieces of fruit, such as cherries or orange, floating in the bottle; 70 proof. Originally sold as a cold remedy.

Rosé (ro-zay)—Pink table wine, dry, medium-sweet, or sweet. Grenache rosé is rosé of the Grenache grape; Gamay rosé is of the Gamay grape, etc. Pink champagne is sometimes labeled Sparkling Rosé.

Saint-Émilion (sant-ay-meel-yon)—French dry, tart red table wine.

Saint-Estèphe (sant-es-tef)—French dry, tart red table wine.

Saint-Julien—French dry, tart red table wine.

Salmanazar—Large wine bottle, equivalent to 12 regular-size bottles.

Sangarees—Tall sugared wine, brandy, or ale drinks, with added water or soda, served with slice of lemon, other fruit, and nutmeg.

Sauterne (so-tairn)—White table wine, dry, medium-sweet, or sweet. French sauternes, spelled with the final *s*, is always sweet.

Sauvignon Blanc (so-veen-yohn blahnk)—Spicy white table wine of the Sauvignon blanc grape; dry, medium-sweet, or sweet.

Schnapps—Hollands gin, or (in Holland and Germany) any distilled liquor.

Sediment—Wine, when aged in the bottle, deposits a sediment or film of grape solids on the glass. It sometimes is called crust or *chemise*.

Semillon (sem-ee-yohn)—A sauterne of the Semillon grape, dry, medium-sweet, or sweet.

Sherry—"Nutty," pale gold or light amber appetizer or dessert wine, dry, slightly sweet, or fully sweet, 17 to 20 per cent in alcoholic content.

Skittles—An old English game played by throwing wooden disks at nine pins; the predecessor of modern bowling. It is traditionally associated with beer drinking; hence the expression "beer and skittles."

Slings—Various sweetened drinks made of spirits or liqueurs and lemon juice, sometimes with added bitters.

Sloe gin—A reddish, sweet liqueur with flavor obtained from the sloe berry (blackthorn bush). Usually 60- to 70-proof.

Small beer—Old English term for weak beer; also for homemade beer. In Colonial times, a thin ale was called small beer.

Smashes—Short drinks made of brandy or other spirits, mint, and sugar; small juleps.

Soave (so-ah-vay)—Italian dry white table wine.

Solera (so-*lay-ra*)—A wine term that refers to the Spanish method of fractional blending, an intricate system of aging wines gradually in batteries of small casks, periodically mixing portions of new wine with old.

Sommelier (so-mel-*yay*)—One in charge of wine service; literally, a wine butler.

Sours—Short drinks made with spirits, lemon juice, and sugar, decorated with orange slice and a cherry.

Southern Comfort—A liqueur of old bourbon whiskey aged with peach cordial; 86- and 100-proof.

Sparkling Burgundy—Red sparkling wine, usually semi-sweet. In the U.S. it is often labeled red champagne.

Sparkling wines—Effervescent wines, such as champagne, that obtain their sparkle from secondary fermentation in closed containers. Also called *mousseux* (French) and *spumante* (Italian). Artificially carbonated wines may not be labeled "sparkling."

Spätlese (shpate-lay-zeh)—*see Auslese.*

Spiritus Frumenti—Whiskey.

"Split"—Small wine bottle, usually 2/5 pint (6.4 fluid ounces) for table wines, or 8 ounces for champagne.

Spritzer—White wine and seltzer.

Spumante—*see* Sparkling wines.

Strega—A yellow, orange-flavored Italian liqueur; 85-proof.

Swedish Punsch—A yellow, rummy liqueur flavored with lemon, tea, and herbs, with a Batavia arrack base.

Swizzles—Short drinks made with rum, crushed ice, sugar, and bitters, stirred by twisting a swizzle stick.

Sylvaner—White table wine of the Sylvaner grape; dry or medium-sweet.

"Table" wines—Inclusive term for all grape wines containing not more than 14 per cent alcohol. Also called "light" wines.

Tavel (ta-vel)—A rosé from the Rhône Valley of France.

Teaspoon—1/8 fluid ounce.

"Teetotalers"—Term for total abstainers. It originated from the rolls of a temperance society in Michigan. When a member pledged total abstinence, the letter "T" was written opposite his name.

"Tenth"—Four-fifth pint bottle; 12.8 fluid ounces, 1/10 gallon. Sometimes called a half-bottle.

Toasting—The custom of drinking to someone's health is an ancient one. In England pieces of toast were put into drinks as a delicacy.

Toddy—Originally meant palm wine, but now also means any mixture of spirits, sweetening, and hot water, usually with spices added.

Tokaj (to-kay)—A group of Hungarian wines that may be red or white, dry or sweet.

Tokay—California pink-amber dessert wine, less sweet than port.

Traminer (trah-*mee*-ner)—White table wine of the Traminer grape; dry or medium-sweet.

Triple Sec—*see* Cointreau.

Trockenbeerenauslese—*see Auslese.*

Valpolicella (vahl-pol-ee-chel-la)—Italian dry, tart red table wine.

Verdicchio—Italian dry white table wine.

Vermouth—Wine flavored with numerous herbs, barks, flowers, leaves, and seeds, 15 to 20 per cent in alcoholic content. The French type is dry and pale amber; the Italian type is sweet and dark amber. The name originated from wormwood, one of its original ingredients, *Wermut* in German. *Wer* means "man," *mut* means courage, spirit, or manhood.

Vin (van)—French word for wine.

Vinho (veen-yo)—Portuguese word for wine.

Vinifera—The great European family of wine-grape varieties, as distinguished from the native American (Labrusca) varieties. Vinifera varieties in the United States grow almost entirely in California and neighboring states and constitute most of the country's production.

Vino (vee-no)—Spanish and Italian word for wine.

Vin Rosé (van ro-*zay*)—Rosé wine.

Vintner—Literally, a wine merchant. Nowadays the term also applies to winery proprietors.

V.F.C.—Very Fine Cognac.

V.O.—Very Old.

Volnay—French red burgundy.

Vodka, flavored—Orange-, lemon-, mint-, grape-, lime-, cherry-, and chocolate-flavored vodkas are sold in some states; usually 70-proof.

V.O.P.—Very Old Pale.

Vosne-Romanée (vone-ro-ma-nay)—French red burgundy.

Vouvray—French white table wine, dry or medium-sweet.

V.S.O.P.—Very Special Old Pale.

V.V.O.—Very, Very Old.

V.S.Q.—Very Special Quality.

V.V.S.O.P.—Very, Very Superior Old Pale.

Wassail—Originally meant, in early England, a good wish while drinking at Christmas or other festivals. It also meant the beverage that was drunk, traditionally an ale or wine flavored with spices, sugar, toast, and roasted crabapples. Nowadays it means the singing of Christmas carols from house to house, or just plain carousing.

White—A wine term that means either straw-colored, golden, or light amber.

White Vermouth—French-type vermouth.

Wineglass—Means 4 fluid ounces to a bartender, but Webster says it is 2 fluid ounces.

Wine spirits—Neutral grape brandy.

XXX—Ancient Egyptian symbol of purity and perfection, used on liquor labels to represent special quality.

Zinfandel—California claret of the Zinfandel grape.

Index

Absinthe, 81–82
Absinthol, 81–82
Absorption, 14–15, 17, 19, 24, 73, 82, 93, 118, 133, 144; from intestine, 15; rates of, 17, 19, 24, 73, 82, 93, 118, 133, 144; from stomach, 15
Abstainers, 4, 16, 77, 139, 182–183
Abyssinia, 6
Accuracy, effect on, 16, 127
Acidosis, 146
Addictive drinkers, 4, 82, 120, 122, 125, 141, 144, 166, 169, 170, 173
Adirondacks experiment, 148–149
"Adjuncts," brewing, 93
Advertisements, 32, 33, 45–46, 54, 63, 64, 71, 92, 95, 99, 110, 113, 116, 149, 160, 182; beer, 92, 95, 99, 160; brandy, 71; gin, 54; vermouth, 113; vodka, 63, 64; wine, 110, 116; whiskey, 45–46, 149, 182
Aftertaste, 41
Age: of beers, 85, 86, 103; of spirits, 32, 33, 34, 37, 38, 41, 42, 46, 48, 50, 52, 53, 54, 58; of wines, 113–114
Aged, alcohol in treatment of the, 16, 129
Age labeling, 46, 52, 53, 103, 114–115
Aging, 34, 40, 52–53, 54, 148; effect on spirits, 34, 52–53, 54, 148; excessive, 34, 40, 52–53
Aguardiente, 58, 187
Airlines, 66, 74, 137–138, 174
Alabama, 178, 188
Alaska, 187, 189
Alchemists, 78, 130
Alcohol, 3, 4, 5, 7, 33, 37, 38, 39, 62–63, 67–69, 125, 126, 148, 149, 187; amyl, 148; boiling point of, 33; in bread, 4; butyl, 148; definition of, 5; ethanol, ethyl, 5, 125, 149; in livestock feed, 5; methyl, 37; in mother's milk, 4; propyl, 148; states where obtainable, 67–69, 187; 200-proof, pure, 126, 187; uses, 5
Alcohol content by weight, 87–88
Alcohol contents: ales, 4, 25, 86, 88; beers, 4, 25, 28, 29, 30, 32, 84, 87, 88, 89, 94, 103, 105–106, 188–189; brandies, 25, 57–58; cocktails, 25, 28, 29, 30, 73, 74; extracts, 4, 68; gins, 23, 25, 54–55; grain neutral spirits, 67; highballs, 5, 25, 28, 29, 30, 52, 73, 74; liqueurs, 25, 79; malt liquor, 87, 88; mead, 107; pulque, 107; rums, 25, 60–61, 68; sake, 107; tequila, 70; whiskeys, 24–25, 30, 50, 51, 52; wines, 4, 25, 28, 29, 30, 32, 116, 119; vermouths, 25; vodkas, 22, 62, 66
Alcohol in Italian Culture, 82, 122
"Alcohol Quotient," 18, 19, 20
Alcoholics Anonymous, 172
Alcoholics, chronic, 133, 139–140, 170–171
Alcoholism, 3, 125, 133, 139–140, 184
Alcoholism Information Centers, 172
Alcool, 69
Aldehydes, 148
Alden, John, 86
Ale, 3, 4, 5, 25, 77, 86–88, 95, 100, 105, 106; stock ale, 86, 105; strengths of, 4, 25, 86, 88
Allen, Joseph, 104
Allergies, 55, 129, 135, 141
Altitude, effect of, 137
American Brewer, 161
Amino acids, 20, 147
Anchor Brewery, 104
Anesthetic, 11, 15, 26
Angelica, 55, 187
Anger, 19, 26
Angostura, 78
Anise, 55, 187
Anisette, 79, 80, 82, 187
Anne, "Good Queen," 56
Antibiotics, 126
Antifreeze, 5, 37, 163
Anti Saloon League, 180
Antiseptics, 5
Anxiety, 127, 132, 144
Apéritifs, 76, 77–78, 116, 129, 158, 161
Aphrodisiacs, 129–131
Appetite, 16, 76, 77–78, 124, 134, 158–159
Apples, 121, 157
Apple brandy; *see* Brandy
Applejack; *see* Brandy
Apple wine; *see* Wine
Apricot, 58, 188; brandy, 58; liqueur, 188
Aquavit, 5, 69, 161
Arab literature, 130
Araq; see Rum
Arizona, 189
Arkansas, 34, 187, 188
Armagnac; *see* Brandy
Arrack; *see* Rum
Arthritis and Rheumatism Foundation, 138
Artichokes, 130
Aspirin, 18, 125, 145, 146
Automatic liquor dispenser, 151

Bad whiskey, 40, 53
Balanced diet, 132, 140, 158, 170
Banana beer, 106
Banquet-strength cocktails, 74
"Bar" liquors, 12
Barbados rum; *see* Rum
Bargains: in bars, 12; beer, 12, 103–104; liquor, 34, 35, 36; wine, 115

Barley, 41, 42, 85, 135; allergy, 135
Bars, 10–13, 21, 23, 24, 30, 36, 40, 43, 44, 70, 74, 75, 85, 95, 96, 100–102, 104, 105, 107, 113, 147, 155, 175, 176, 179, 182, 183
Bathtub gin, 37, 56, 182
Bavarian beer, 94, 105
Beading oil, 37, 40
Beatniks, 128
Beer, 3–7, 11–15, 19–33, 47, 63, 69, 74, 76, 84–107, 112, 118–119, 132, 135, 147–148, 150, 154, 164, 168; aging, 85, 86; alcohol content, 4, 22, 25, 28, 29, 30, 32, 84, 86, 87, 88, 105–106, 188–189; banana beer, 106; Bavarian, 94, 105; beer garden, 85; "beer times," 85; blandness trend, 84; bock, 86, 95, 105; bottles, 104, 107; bubbles in, 84, 87; calories in, 85, 157, 160, 161; Canadian, 86-88; cans, 84, 87; care of, 102–103; cola-flavored, 106; dark, 86; depots, 104; draught, 84, 86; effects of, 14, 87, 89–92, 93, 118–120, 134; flavored, 86, 106; food value, 96, 102, 158; Japanese, 94; labels, 86–88; lager, 86–88; Mexican, 94; Münchener, 105; near beer, 91; origin of, 84; pilsner, 86; quantities drunk, 22, 89; steam beer, 104–105; wheat beer, 106
Behavior, 16, 19, 26, 27, 73, 133, 151
Benedictine, 79, 189
Benzedrine, 6, 141, 147
Berkson, Dr. Joseph, 127
Berlin, 106
Bible, The, 119
Birdsall, Bergen, 179
Bitterness, 34, 40, 78, 85, 86, 92, 93, 105, 106, 134, 158; beer, 85, 86, 92, 93, 105, 106, 158; whiskeys, 34, 40; wines, 78, 158
Bitters, 21, 77–78
Blackberry-flavored brandy; *see* Brandy
"Blackouts," 171
Black Velvet, 106
Blandness trend, 51, 54, 66, 84, 92–95, 97, 99, 103, 106, 113; beers, 66, 84, 92–95, 97, 106; gin, 54, 66; whiskeys, 51, 66; vermouths, 113; vodka, influence of, 66; wine, 66
Blended whiskey, 3, 41, 42, 43, 44–46, 50, 147–149
Blending, 114, 117
"Blind" tastings, 44, 62, 94, 96, 98, 102, 110
Blood-alcohol levels, 4, 17, 19, 22, 23, 24, 27–31, 72, 89, 118, 131–134; from beer, 19, 22, 28, 29, 89; from cocktails, 19, 22, 28, 29; of drunken drivers, 22–23; normal without drinking, 4; from whiskey, 19, 22, 28, 29, 72; from wine, 22, 28, 29
Blood pressure, 137
Blood-sugar level, 26, 27, 73
Bloody Mary, 64, 155
Bock, 86, 95, 105
"Body," 87, 92–93, 99, 189
Body chemistry, 19, 143, 149
Body controls, 16, 143
Body weight, 18, 19, 20, 28–31
Boilermaker, 134
Boiling point of alcohol, 33
Bootlegging; *see* Moonshine
Bootleg liquor; *see* Moonshine
"Booze," 6, 166–167
Bordeaux, 111
Borneo, 6
Boston, 75
Bottled in bond, 25, 50, 51–52, 58, 134, 160
Bottled cocktails, 74, 154
Bottled highballs, 74
Bottles: balthazar, 188; beer, 102, 104, 107; Canadian sizes, 36; colored, protection by, 115; destruction of, 36, 37; fifth, 36, 192; half pints, 80; jeroboam, 194; magnum, 195; methusaleh, 195; nebuchadnezzar, 196; pint, 36; quart, 36, 104; rehoboam, 197; salmanazar, 197; shorties, 104; split, 199; tenth, 36, 199; wine, 114, 115
Bouilleurs de cru, 121
Bourbon, 3, 11, 12, 37, 41, 42, 43, 44, 46, 47, 49–50, 53, 66, 70–71, 80, 134, 135, 147, 161; exports, 70–71; origin of, 49; taste, 41, 49–50, 66
Bourbon County, Kentucky, 49
Bourbon Institute, 41, 70–71
"Bourbon liqueur," 80
Bouza, 6
Bracers, 74
Brain, 15, 130, 143
Brandewijn, 57
Brands, 12, 13, 32, 34, 35, 36, 51, 88, 95, 102, 103, 132
Brandy, 5, 24–25, 33, 37, 41, 57–60, 71, 79, 108, 109, 119, 121, 148, 151, 153, 154, 157, 161, 193; age, 58, 60; alcoholic contents, 24–25, 57–58; apple, applejack, 58–59; apricot, 58; armagnac, 58; blackberry, 58; California, 57–58; calories in, 157, 161; calvados, 59; cherry, 58–59; cognac, 37, 57–59, 71; *eau de vie de marc,* 58; "Fine Champagne," 59; flavors of, 57–60; fruit-flavored, 58, 193; "Grande Champagne," 59; grappa, 58; how made, 33; "imported French," 58; kirschwasser, 59; marc, 58; "Napoleon brandy," 59–60; peach, 58; Peruvian, 58; "Petite Champagne," 59; Pisco, 58; plum, 59; slivovitz, 41, 59; Spanish, 58; straight, 58; wine in, 109; in Wisconsin, 71
Brandywine, 57
Bratwurst, 85
Bread, 4, 42, 85, 111, 157, 162; alcohol in, 4
Breakfast clubs, 36
Breast feeding, 3, 140
Breath, 17, 63, 124, 136
Breweries, 85, 88, 92–96, 98–99, 103, 107, 115; number of, 103; workers in, 85
Brewing, 85, 86, 92–96, 98
"Brewster," 96
"Bride ale," 97
Britain, 6, 38–39, 47, 48, 54, 56, 62, 70, 85, 86, 97, 100, 101, 105, 106, 109, 126, 127, 180, 185
British Columbia, 6, 184
British Guiana, 61
British proof, 39
Brittany, 120
Brokers, 35
Bromo-Seltzer, 4
Bronfman, Samuel, 64
Brut, 113
Bubbles, 3, 73, 99–101, 116; in beer, 3, 99–101; in wine, 116
Buffalo grass, 65
Bulk-fermented champagne, 154
Bulk spirits, 35
Burgundy, 25, 111, 112, 114, 119, 190
"Burns more," 32, 37, 44
Businessman's dilemma, 3, 20, 155
Butter, 157
Byrrh, 78, 116

Cactus, 6, 69, 107
Caffeine, 63, 128; added to whiskey, 128
California, 44, 50, 57–58, 67, 68, 109, 114, 117, 175, 188–189; brandy, 57–58; wine, 109, 114
California Temperance Federation, 179
"Call whiskey," 12
Calories, 85, 132, 140, 157–162; beer, 85, 157, 160, 161; cocktails, 157, 160, 161; drink-calorie table, 161; liqueurs, 161; spirits, 157, 160, 161; wines, 157, 159, 160, 161
Calso, 155
Calvados; *see* Brandy
Campari, 78, 190
Canada, 12, 33, 36, 39, 42, 43, 44, 45–47, 50, 51, 52, 53, 62, 66, 68–69, 86, 88, 94, 95, 98, 178; bottle sizes, 36; home brewing legal, 98; proof spirits, 33, 39
Canadian beers, 86, 88, 94, 95
Canadian whiskey, 12, 42, 43, 45–47, 50, 51, 52, 53
Canon Law Society of America, 181
Cans, beer, 84, 87, 100, 102–103, 104, 107
Cantharides, 130
Capillaries, 16
Caramel, 33, 37, 51
Caraway seed, 69
Carbonation, 73, 85, 102, 104, 112, 116; effect of, 73; of beers, 102, 104; of wine, 116
Carbon dioxide, 73, 99, 116
Carbon monoxide, 126
Care: of beer, 102–103; of wine, 115
Caribbean Indians, 5
Cassia, 55
Catholic Church, 181
Causes of problem drinking, 140–141
Central nervous system, 15, 16, 140
Century plant, 69
Champagne, 106, 109, 111–113, 116, 153–154, 160, 161, 174; punch, 153
Chancellor, C. W., 121
Changing flavors, 8, 33, 51, 54, 84, 87, 92–95, 97
Charcoal filtered, 63, 190
Charente, 59
Charred barrels, 41, 42, 47–49, 53; origin of, 49
Chartreuse, 79, 190
Chaser: beer, 69, 134; water, 72, 134
Cheap whiskey, 34, 35
Cheese, 5, 152
Cherry: brandy, 58–59; liqueur, 190
Children, drinking by, 163–169
Chills, 129, 137
China, 6, 33, 68, 70, 106, 111, 130; liquors of, 6, 68, 70
Chlorine, 125
Chloroform, 142
Choko, 6
Cholestorol, 138
Churches, attitudes toward drinking, 180–181
Cider, 48, 59, 190–191
Cinchona, 78
Cirrhosis, 139
Claret, 119, 157, 191
Clergy, drinking by, 180
Coca-Cola, 100, 116
Cocktail hour, 82
Cocktail parties, 3, 20, 133, 150, 153, 154, 183
Cocktails, 12, 19–21, 23–26, 28–30, 54–56, 65, 74–76, 79, 82–83, 120, 132–133, 138, 157, 160–162, 166; banquet-strength, 74; bottled, 74; definition of, 74; effects of, 23–24, 83, 133, 160; at lunchtime, 83; origin, 74; strength of, 21–25, 28–30, 73–74
Coffee, 17, 63, 92, 114, 128, 141, 145, 147, 194
Cognac; *see* Brandy
Cognac oil, 59
Cola, 100, 106, 116, 128, 160, 161
Colds, 138
College students, 85, 163, 166, 185
Collins, 24, 55, 73, 161, 191
Colorado, 187, 189
Colors of beverages, 33, 37–38, 42, 49, 51, 54, 64, 65, 69, 70, 81, 108, 113
Columbus, 5
Commission des Liqueurs de Québec, 69
"Community Veto," 180
Concord grape, 117
Conduct, 16, 19, 26, 27, 73
Confidence, 16
Congeners, 147–149
Connecticut, 176, 187, 189
Connoisseur lore, 108, 110, 114
Consumption: beer, 84, 92–93, 117; spirits, 117; wine, 117
Contest, barrel disposal, 47
Convalescent, 16
Conventions, drinking at, 20, 73
Convicts, 6
Conway, Monsignor J. D., 181
Cooking, 79, 85, 109, 162
Cooling drinks, 137
Coordination, 16, 19, 127
Cordials; *see* Liqueurs
Coriander, 55
Corn, 5, 37–38, 41, 42, 49, 92, 135; allergy, 135
Corn whiskey, 37–38, 41, 42
Cossacks, 65
Cost of spirits, 34, 46
Craig, Reverend Elijah, 49
Cream, 20
Crème de Cacao, 79, 181
Crème de Menthe, 80–81, 191; recipe for, 80–81
Creosote, 37
Crocodile, 130
Crown cap, 107
Cru, 192
Cuban rum; *see* Rum
Cuba Libre, 161
Cultural patterns, 141, 181, 184
Culture in History, 142
Curaçao, 80, 192

Daiquiri, 60, 161
Danger signals, 3, 170–172
Danger zone, 29
Dark beer, 86, 95, 105
Dayton, Ohio, 27
Death from drinking, 27
De Gaulle, Charles, 121
Delaware, 36, 189
Delaware grape, wine, 192
Demerara rum; *see* Rum
Demi-sec, 113
Denmark, 80, 107, 111
Depressant effect, 15, 16, 127, 128
Desserts, 61, 79, 154, 162; flaming, 61, 154
Dessert wines, 25, 108, 161, 192
Destruction of bottles, 36, 37
Dickens, Charles, 48

Diet, 3, 90, 96, 122, 132, 140, 157–162, 170; balanced diet, 132, 140, 158, 170; deficient diet, 140
"Dietetically non-fattening," 160
Different labels, same whiskey, 35
Digestifs, 79
Digestion, 14, 76, 124
Dilution, effect of, 11, 14, 17, 24, 72, 73, 76, 133, 181; by gastric juices, 14, 72
Dinner: drinking before, 20, 26, 72, 73, 82–83, 120, 138, 153; drinking after, 20, 26, 79; with wine, 73, 154
"Distilled and bottled by," 35
Distilled gin, 54
Distillers, 32, 33, 35, 37, 38, 41, 42, 45–49, 50, 52, 71, 74, 115
Distilling: definition, 33; history of, 33, 40; illegal at home, 33; in prisons, 6
District of Columbia, 174, 187, 189
Diuretic, 55, 132
Dizziness, 16, 23, 90, 141, 146
Doctors, drinking by, 126
Draught beer, 84, 86, 95, 99, 101–102, 104
Dreams, 128
Drink-calorie table, 161
Drinkers, number of, 3, 4
Drinking, motives for, 5, 7, 8, 63, 64, 90, 92, 96, 118, 172
Drinkometer, 28, 30
"Drip-dry" states, 178
Driving, 22–23, 30–31, 87, 90, 126, 127, 133, 143, 152–153; tests, 126, 127
Dropsy, 140
Druggists, 37, 56, 65, 68
"Drunk for a penny," 56
"Dry," 24, 112–113
Dry gin, 54
Dubonnet, 78, 116
Duplicator fluid, 6
Dutch gin, 55
Dyak, 6
Dyspepsia, 72

Eau de vie, 57
Eau de vie de marc; see Brandy
Education, 165–166, 180
Edward VIII, King, 109–110
Efficiency, 83, 124, 126
Egg, 20, 130, 152
Eggnog, 77
80-proof whiskeys, 25, 36, 39, 51, 52, 151
Einbecker, 105
Election day drinking, 175
Elimination from body, 17, 19–20, 24, 137–138, 145; in breath, 17, 137–138; in perspiration, 17, 145; in urine, 17
Elixirs, 78
Elizabeth II, Queen, 183
Elderberry wine, 25
Emotions, 27, 130, 139
Épernay, 59
Episcopal Church, 180
Esophagus, 14
Essences, essential oils, 37, 79, 81, 130
Estate bottled, 115, 192
Esters, 52, 118, 148
Ethanol, 5, 125, 149
Ether, 128, 142
Ethers, 52
Excitement, 26
Executives, drinking by, 83
Extracts, alcoholic, 4, 68, 78, 79
Eyesight, 16, 30, 127

Fallacies, 143
Fatal dose, 27
Fatigue, 19, 26, 82, 127, 128, 138, 143
Federal Food and Drug Administration, 164
Fennel, 55
Fermentation, 84, 85, 86, 192
Fever, 139
Fifth; *see* Bottles
"Fine Champagne"; *see* Brandy
Finland, 127
Fish, 130, 152
Fizzes, 24, 135, 193
Flannagan, Betsy, 74
Flavored gins, 55
Flavored vodkas, 200
Flavors, non-alcoholic, 65
Flips, 60, 193
Florida, 163, 175, 187, 189
Flying, effect while, 137
Foam aids, 99
Foam, on beer, 84, 87, 99–101, 105
Food, 5, 9, 10, 16, 17, 20, 25, 82, 92–93, 96, 107, 108, 133, 144, 146, 152, 158; alcohol as a, 9, 16, 92–93, 96, 107, 108, 158; effect of, 10, 17, 20, 25, 133, 144, 146, 152
Food stores, sale in, 96, 175
Forbidden: charm of, 7, 64, 165; when drinking is, 139
Forbidden Fruit, 80, 193
"Foxy," 117, 193
France, 58, 59, 60, 70–71, 76, 80, 81, 110–111, 114, 120–121; wines of, 110–111; *see also* Appendix
Franklin, Benjamin, 120
Fraternities, 164
French Government, 110
Furfural, 148
Fusel oil, 148

Gallup Poll, 182
Gamay, 112, 193
Gantt, Dr. W. Horsley, 16
Garlic, 130
Garrecht, Hugh, 7
Garrett, Captain Paul, 117
Gasoline, 141
Gas stations, sale in, 175
Gastric juices, 14
Gastritis, 14, 72
Gelatine, 97
Genever, geneva gin, 55
Genièvre, 54
Genius, 126, 127
Georgetown, Kentucky, 49
Georgia, 129–130, 178, 187, 188
Georgia, Soviet, 65
German migration, 86
Germany, 86, 95, 105, 106, 114, 127; beers of, 95, 105, 106; wines of, 114
Geshu plant, 6
Gibson cocktail, 76
Gimlet, 65, 76, 135
Gin, 11, 12, 23–25, 37, 41, 54–56, 64, 66, 69, 75–76, 113, 148, 154, 164, 166; after beer, 11; age of, 54; alcoholic contents, 23, 25, 54, 55; bathtub, 37, 56, 182; blandness trend, 54, 66; calories in, 157, 161; compounded, 54; distilled, 54; dry, 54; Dutch, 55; effects of, 23–24, 55–56, 118, 133; flavored, 55; geneva, genever, 55; herbs in, 55; London dry, 54–55; Old Town, 55; Plymouth, 55; yellow, 54

Ginger, 116, 130
Ginger ale, 13, 106, 154, 155, 160, 161
Glands, 125, 138
Glasses: for beer, 85, 100–101; cleaning of, 100–101; sizes of, 11; wineglass, 75, 200
Glycerin, 37, 56, 79
Goldsmith, Oliver, 126, 127
"Good farewell," 41
"Good" whiskey, 40–41
Gourmet organizations, 109
Gout, 139
"Government supervision," 50–51
Grain neutral spirits; *see* Neutral spirits
Grains, 41, 47, 48–49, 57, 65, 84, 85, 92–93
Grain whiskey, 45–46, 48, 134
"Grande Champagne"; *see* Brandy
Grapes, 57, 58, 59, 68, 108, 109, 111–112, 115, 117, 121, 135; allergy, 135; jellies, 117; juices, 68, 108, 117; varieties, 117
Grappa; *see* Brandy
Greeks, 6, 68
Green Muse, 81–82
Greenberg, Dr. Leon A., 18, 20, 21, 23, 30, 129
Groaning beer, 97
Grog, 57, 62, 194
Guests, 150–155; dinner, 153; intoxicated, 152; non-drinking, 152–153
Guilt feelings, 7, 144, 166–167, 174, 181
Gulab, 77
Gunpowder proof, 38

Habitual excessive drinkers, 170
Hair lotions, 5
"Hair of the dog," 145
Haitian rum; *see* Rum
Hammurabi, King, 155
Hangover, 4, 13, 142, 143–149, 185; champagne, 147; "cures," 13, 143, 145, 149; gin, 147; "preventives," 13, 143, 146, 149; remorse in, 144; Scotch, 147; thirst during, 143, 144, 146; treatment of, 145
Hashish, 130
Hawaii, 70, 189
Hayakawa, Dr. Samuel I., 165
Hayes, Juan, 44
Headache, 135, 143, 144, 147, 149
Head hunters, 6
Hearing, 127
Heart, 15, 16, 78, 138, 139
Heart disease, 16, 138, 139
Henderson, Professor Yandell, 73–74
Henius, Henry R., 99
Henry, O., 26
Herbs, 55, 68, 79, 81, 107, 113, 116, 130, 158
Heredity, 140
Heroin, 165
Hiccups, 135–136
Hindu literature, 130
Highballs, 5, 11, 14, 19, 20–25, 28–31, 72–74, 79, 118, 133, 135, 160–161; bottled, 74; effects of, 11, 14, 24, 72, 133, 160–161; strength of, 5, 21, 24–25, 28–30, 73
Highland whisky, 47
"High proof," 45, 58
High-school students, 163, 164
Hillbillies, 36, 37
Hip flasks, 138, 184
Hollands gin, 55, 69
"Hollow leg," 25–26
Home assortments, 154
Home brew, 93, 96–98; illegal, 97; legal in Canada, 98
Homemade: beer, 93, 96–98; cider, 98; liqueurs, 68, 80–81; wine, 98, 109
Home-mixed drinks, 11, 21, 77, 151, 155
Homer, 126
Honey, 6, 57, 77, 84, 86, 107
Hops, 85, 86, 92, 94, 97, 99, 104, 105, 106
Hors d'oeuvres: breadstuffs, 152; cheese dips, spreads, 152; egg, 20, 152; fish, 152; meat, 20; nuts, 10, 152; popcorn, 10, 152; pretzels, 152; sausage, 152
"Horse's neck," 155
Hosts, 3, 11, 21, 77, 150–156
Hot dogs, 85, 93
Hotels, 21
Hunger, effect of, 19, 26
"Hydrolics," 142

Ice, 11, 21, 23, 73, 74, 76, 77, 152, 154
Idaho, 188
Ill from drinking, 26, 135, 184
Illinois, 36, 50, 67, 174, 175, 176, 187, 189
Imitation whiskey, 37
Immune, 26
"Imported French brandy," 58
Importers, 46
Imports, 80, 85, 88, 93–95, 100, 105, 110–112; beers, 85, 88, 93–95, 100, 105; wines, 110–112
Incas, 5
India, 6, 185
Indiana, 50, 175, 189
Indians, 5, 6
Inhaling alcohol, 16
Inhibitions, 15–16, 27, 127, 130–131, 159
Injected alcohol, 16–17, 126
Insomnia, 128
Instant whiskey, 48
Internal Revenue Service, 50, 98
Intestine, absorption from, 15
Intolerance of drunkenness, 185
Intoxication, 8, 14, 16, 17, 19, 22, 27, 89, 90, 136; definitions, 19, 22, 27, 89, 90, 136
Iodine, 37, 42
Iowa, 174, 188
Irish, drinking by, 166, 185
Irish Coffee, 128, 194
Irish whiskey, 41, 42, 48, 51, 53, 130
Irritant, 14, 72, 134, 136
Italians, drinking by, 76, 108, 122, 159, 166
Italy, 76, 80, 108, 122, 159

Jamaica rum; *see* Rum
Japan, 86, 94, 106; beer of, 94
Jefferson, Thomas, 120
Jerez, 111
Jews, drinking by, 166, 185
Jigger, 21, 155, 194
Johns Hopkins University, 16
Johnson, Dr. Harry J., 82–83
Judgment affected, 26, 30, 127
Julep, 77, 161
Juniper oil, 37, 54–56
Juniver, 54
Juvenile delinquency, 164

Kansas, 178, 187, 189
Kau-yang-tsyew, 6
Kava, 6
Kegs, 99, 104, 105
Kentucky, 43, 46, 49–50, 67, 175, 178, 187, 189; distillers of, 46, 49–50

Khrushchev, Nikita, 122
Kidney stimulant, 55
Kinnier-Wilson, S. A., 7
Kirschwasser; *see* Brandy
Koran, 7
Krausened, 104
Kümmel, 80, 194

Labels, 8, 25, 33, 35, 36, 38, 42, 43, 45–47, 50, 53, 58, 74, 86–88, 111–114, 115; beer, 86–88; brandy, 58; gin, 54–55; rum, 60; whiskey, 33, 43, 45–47, 50, 53; wine, 111–114, 115, 116
Lager, 86–88, 103, 105
Lamb flesh, 6
Laplanders, 6
"Last drink," 11
Laxative, 78, 145
Lemert, Edwin, 184
Lemon extract, 68
Lewis, Joe E., 53
Licensed stores, 35
Licorice, 48, 81, 82
Life Extension Foundation, 83
"Lightning" stopper, 107
"Light" Scotches, 51
Lime juice, 69, 76
Lining your stomach, 20
Liqueur de la Pendule, 68
Liqueurs, 5, 25, 54, 76, 78–82, 130, 161; calories in, 161; cordials, meaning of, 78; glycerin in, 79; homemade, 79–81; origin of, 78, 130; strengths of, 25, 79; sweetness of, 79; uses, 76, 78, 79, 82; *see also* Appendix
"Liquid bread," 85
Liquor dispenser, automatic, 151
Liquors, cost of, 13
Liver, 15, 17, 25, 31, 138, 139, 147; diseases, 139; oxidation by, 15, 17, 25, 31, 147
Livestock feeds, 5
Local prohibition, 178, 180
Loeb, Dr. Edwin, 142
Lolli, Dr. Giorgio, 82
"London dry," 54–55
Long drinks, effect of, 24
Longevity, 4
Lord, Bishop John Wesley, 180
Louisiana, 177, 188
Love potions, 78, 130
Low-sodium diets, 96
Lucia, Dr. Salvatore P., 119
Lunch-time cocktail, 83, 136
Lungs, 17, 137–138
Lupulin, 92, 158
Lynndale Distillery Co., 38

Macbeth, 131
Mace, 141
Madeira, 114, 195
Magellan, 5
Maguey, 6, 107
Maine, 175, 189
Maize, 5
Malt, 42, 85, 87, 92–93, 94, 97, 104, 105
Malt liquor, 86–88
Manhattans, 12, 21, 24–25, 30, 133, 134, 154, 160, 161; effect of, 133, 160, 161; strength of, 21, 24–25
Mankind, drinking by, 5, 8, 90, 92, 126, 181
Manners, 182–185
Maraschino, 154, 195
Marc; see Brandy
Marshall, Admiral William J., 70
Martin, John, 64
Martinez cocktail, 75
Martini, 4, 11, 12, 23, 24, 27, 54–56, 65, 70, 74–75, 76, 113, 133, 134, 151, 154, 160–161, 182; calories in, 160–161; effect of, 23–24, 55, 133, 134; extra dry, 23–24, 75, 76, 113; olive in, 76; original recipe, 75; shadow Martini, 75; strength of, 23–25; tequila Martini, 70; whisper Martini, 75
Martinique rum; *see* Rum
Maryland, 36, 43, 44, 175, 177, 187, 189
Massachusetts, 163, 175, 188
Masticha, 68, 195
Mathé, Dr. Charles Pierre, 68
Mayflower, 86
Mayo Clinic, 125
Mead, 5, 6, 86, 107
Measuring liquor, 11, 21, 77, 151
Meat, 5, 6, 20, 152
Medical College of Virginia, 149
Medicinal whiskey, 43
Medicines, alcoholic, 4, 5, 68, 78
Memory, 127
Mendès-France, Pierre, 120
Metabolism, 25
Methodists, 180
Methyl alcohol, 37
Metropolis Hotel, 75
Mexico, 6, 9, 69, 86, 94, 107; beers of, 94
Mezcal, 107, 195
Michigan, 36, 137, 189
Mickey Finn, 66
Milk, 4, 5, 6, 7, 8, 20, 73, 92, 100, 105, 157, 160; intoxicating drinks made of, 6; mother's milk, 4
Milk Industry Foundation, 7
Milwaukee, 95, 100, 105
Minerals, 158
Minimum ages for purchase, 176
Minnesota, 88, 189
Mint, 77
Mint extract, 80–81
Mississippi, 177, 188
Missouri, 67, 187, 189
"Mixing your drinks," 11
"Mocktails," 165
Moderate drinking definition, 8
Modern technology, 47, 65, 98
Mohammedans, 7
Molasses, 57, 60–61, 70
"Momism," 141
Monopoly states, 35, 175
Montana, 188
Moods, effect of, 26, 27, 133
Moonshine, 6, 12, 34, 36, 37, 38, 40, 56, 67, 79, 120–121, 175, 181; legal in France, 120–121
Morphine, 165
Moscow Mule, 76
Moslems, 7
Mosley, Bishop J. Brooke, 181
Mother Goose, 96–97
Mother's milk, 4
Mount Vernon, 48, 97
Mouth, 139
Mouthwashes, 5
Münchener, 105
Munich, 105
Muscles, 16, 127; coordination, 16, 19, 127
Mushrooms, 130

Mustard seed, 130
Mutton, 130

Naked Martini, 55
Namoluk, 6
"Napoleon brandy"; *see* Brandy
Narcotic effect, 7, 15
Narcotics, 7, 81, 141–142
Nasal inhalers, 164
Nation, Carry, 179
National Council on Alcoholism, 173
National Institute of Mental Health, 184
National Safety Council, 30
Nature, 113
Nausea, 26, 89
Near beer, 91, 95–96
"Neat," 14, 72
Nebraska, 187, 189
Nelson, Lord, 126
Nephritis, 139
Nerves, 82, 118, 128, 129, 140
Netherlands, 56
Neuralgia, 126
Neutral spirits, 42, 45–46, 62–63; in Canadian whiskey, 42, 45–46; in Irish whiskey, 46; on labels, 45–46; in Scotch, 42, 45–46
Nevada, 178, 187, 189
New Brunswick, 68
New England rum; *see* Rum
New Hampshire, 175, 188
New Jersey, 36, 176, 187, 189; Department of Law and Public Safety, 29, 30
New Mexico, 6, 187, 189
New Orleans, 75
New spirits, 37–38
New whiskey, 33, 52, 148
New York, 36, 43, 67, 75, 80, 109, 175, 176, 189
Ng ka pei, 70
Nightcap, 128
Nitrous oxide, 142
Nomenclature of wines, 111–113
Nondrinkers, 4, 136, 152–153, 173
Nonsmokers, 4
Normandy, 120
North Carolina, 37–38, 175, 176, 178, 187, 188; Alcohol Control Board, 37–38
North Dakota, 34, 175, 176, 187, 188
Norway, 22, 24, 127
Nose, red, 16
Nursing a drink, 155
Nutmeg, 48, 141
Nuts, 10, 152

Obesity, 159
Office of Civilian Defense, 129
Offspring, effect on, 3, 124, 131–132, 140
Ohio, 109, 189
Oklahoma, 175, 178, 187, 189
Okolehao, 41, 70
Old-fashioned cocktails, 19, 21, 24–25, 30, 161
Old Tom gin, 55
Olive, in Martini, 76
Olive oil, 20
Onions, 76, 130
Ontario Liquor Control Board, 69
"O.P.," 39
Opium, 130, 165
Orange, 64, 68, 116, 163; spirits of, 37
Oregon, 188–189
Ostracism, power of, 184, 185
Overpriced liquors, 13
Oxidation rate, 15, 17, 19–20, 24, 25, 31, 72, 147
Oxygen, 137, 141, 146–147
Oysters Rockefeller, 82

Pain, 16, 128, 138
Paint solvent, 5, 6, 37, 141, 148
Palm wine, 5, 6
Palomino, 112
Parents, 163–169
Passing out, 27, 128
Peach: brandy, 58; liqueur, 68
Peanuts, 10
Peat, 42, 47
Pellagra, 140
Penicillin, 125
Pennsylvania, 36, 43, 44, 49, 67, 95, 175, 187, 189
Pepper, 65, 130
Peppermint schnapps, 68, 196
Pepper plant, 6
Perfumes, 5
Perspiration, 16, 138, 145
Peru, 5, 58
"Petite Champagne"; *see* Brandy
Petroleum, 65
Pewter, 101
Pharmacopoeia, 79
Philippines, 5
Philosophers' stone, 78
Phlegmatic people, 26
Picnics, beer at, 85, 104
Pilgrims, 86
Pilsner, 86
Pima, 6
Pinot Noir, 112, 196
Piquette, 109
Pineapple juice, 146
Pint; *see* Bottles
Pisadores, 112
Pisco; *see* Brandy
Pisco sour, 58
Pizarro, 5
Placebos, 27
Plastic cement sniffing, 164
Pliny, 124
Plum brandy; *see* Brandy
Plymouth gin, 55
Poe, Edgar Allan, 127
Poi, 70
Poisons, 125–126
Police, 87, 163, 164
Politics, 46, 60
Polyneuropathy, 140
Pony, 21, 75, 104, 155, 196
Popcorn, 10, 152
Port, 25, 111, 112, 114, 119, 139, 197
Porter, 5, 86, 106
Portugal, 111, 112
Potato, 65, 135; allergy, 135; spirits, 65
Potato chips, 10
Pot still, 42, 48, 59, 197
"Prairie oyster," 145
Pregnancy, drinking during, 131–132
Preservative, 126
Pretzels, 152
Price posting, 35
Prices, 12, 13, 32, 33, 34, 35, 60, 65, 67, 69, 93, 97, 111, 114, 115, 120; of alcohol, 67, 69; apéritifs, 13; in bars, 12, 13; beer, 93, 97; brandy, 13; liqueurs, 13; rum, 60; whiskey, 12, 34, 35, 52, 65; wine, 13, 111, 114, 115, 120

Primitive man, 5, 14, 84, 142
Prince Edward Island, 68
Priscilla, 86
Prisons, 6, 141
Private brands, 35
Problem drinking, 4, 7, 73, 140–141, 170–173, 185; causes of, 73, 140–141, 171–172; definitions, 170; number of addicts, 4; treatment of, 173
Prohibition, 37, 43, 56, 68, 79, 95, 107, 178, 182; local, 178; origin of, 180
Prohibitionists, 4, 87, 125, 165, 166, 178–180; changing tactics of, 179–180; finances, 179
"Proof," 33, 35, 38–39
Protein, 20, 93, 99, 126, 140, 158
Prune juice, 37, 51
Prunes, 6
Puerto Rican rum; *see* Rum
Pulque, 6, 107
Punches, 60, 61, 197
Puritans, 48
Pyloric valve, 15, 26

Quality, 12, 32, 34, 35, 40–41, 50, 66, 110–111, 114, 115
Quart; *see* Bottles
Québec, 68–69
Quinine, 78, 155

Radiation, 129
Railroad club cars, 74
Raisins, 6, 37, 60
Randolph, Dr. Theron, 135, 141
Recipes, 68, 77, 79, 80, 81, 97, 153
Rectal administration, 16
Rectifier bottlers, 35
Regulations, 41, 46, 48, 63, 87, 88, 94, 114, 138, 174
Reims, 59
Reindeer milk, 6
Reinheitsgebot, 94
Relaxing effect, 7, 8, 15, 19, 27, 83, 84, 118–119, 138
Research appropriation, 125
Resentment, 27
Restaurants, 13, 112, 155, 175
Retailers, 12, 32, 34, 35, 40, 65, 67, 80, 87, 95, 96, 112, 115, 153, 175, 176
Reused barrels, 42, 46, 53
Rhode Island, 189
Rice, 6, 61, 70, 85, 92
Rock and Rye, 80, 197
"Rocks," on the, 72
Roosevelt, Mrs. Eleanor, 183
Rosé, 114, 197
Rosenstiel, Lewis S., 74
"Royal poverty," 56
Rum, 5, 25, 37, 41, 48, 57, 60–62, 67, 68, 109, 148, 154, 157, 160, 161, 164; alcoholic contents, 25, 60–61; *araq*, 61; arrack, 41, 61; Barbados, 60; Batavia arrack, 61; calories, 157, 160, 161; Cuban, 60; Demerara, 60–61; Haitian, 60; history, 61–62; Jamaican, 60; Martinique, 60; New England, 61; price of, 60; Puerto Rican, 60; Santo Domingo, 60; Trinidad, 60; Virgin Islands, 60; wine in, 60, 109
Rum and brandy, 61
Russia, 22, 65–66, 122, 142; vodka of, 65–66, 122; vodka servings, 22, 66; wine use favored, 122
Rye, 32, 41, 42, 43–44, 46, 48, 53, 63, 135, 147; allergy, 135; confusion about, 43–44
"Rye liqueur," 80

Sacramento, California, 176
Saffron, 48, 130
Saint Bernard dog, 57
St. John's bread, 51
St. Patrick, 48
St. Raphael, 78, 116
Sake, 86, 106–107
Salt, 10, 18, 69, 84, 101, 125; in beer, 84, 101
Samshu, 106
San Francisco, 75, 110, 129, 163
Sangarees, 77, 198
Santo Domingo rum; *see* Rum
Saudi Arabia, 7
Sausage, 152
Sauterne, 111–112, 198; Sauternes, village of, 111
Sauvignon Blanc, 112, 198
Sawdust, 65
Sazerac cocktail, 82
Scandinavia, 69, 184–185
Schenley, 74
Schiedam, 55
Schnapps, 55, 198
Schools, 165–166, 180
"Scotch cow," 73
Scotch whisky, 3, 11, 13, 37, 42, 43, 44, 45–48, 51, 53, 66, 73, 134, 154; "American Scotch," 47; after bourbon, 11; "creeps up," 134; distilleries, 45–48; "light" Scotch, 51; "Scotch type," 47
Screwdriver, 64, 76
Seagram, House of, 64
Sec, 112
Secondhand barrels, 42, 46, 51, 53
Sedative effect, 15, 16, 132, 138
Self-esteem, 16
Self-importance, 7
Seltzer, 21, 76
Semillon, 112, 198
Serianni, Dr. Emidio, 82
Sex stimulation, 78, 124, 129–131
Shadow Martini, 75
Shakespeare, William, 131
Shandygaff, 106
Shaving lotion, 5, 7
Sherry, 13, 19, 51, 57–58, 60, 111, 112, 114, 162, 198
"Shirley Temples," 165
Shock, 136–137
Shopping, 35, 115
Siebel Institute of Technology, 98
Simple syrup, 79, 80
Sin, 7, 8, 166, 181
Singh, Rajendra, 185
Skaal, 69
Skin, 16
Skin conductance, 91, 118
Skink, 130
Slave trade, 61
Sleep, 3, 120, 124, 128, 129, 145; sleeping pills, 128
Slings, 77, 198
Slivovitz; *see* Brandy
Sloe gin, 54, 198
Smelling salts, 136
Smirnoff, 64
Smoking, 4, 131, 136, 144, 167; nonsmokers, 4

Smoky taste, 37, 42, 51
Smoothing agents, 40, 51, 57
"Smuggled," 36
Snake bite, 124, 136–137
Snifters, 57
Snobbery, 32, 85, 111
Sobering time, 24, 30–31
Sociability, 7, 8
Social pressure, 165
Soda, 154, 155, 160
Soda pop, 7
Soft drinks, 77, 112, 153
Sour mash, 32, 50
Sours, 73, 161, 198
South Carolina, 187, 188
South Dakota, 187, 189
Southern Comfort, 80, 198
South Sea natives, 6
Spain, 58, 77, 111, 112; brandy of, 58; wine of, 111, 112
Sparkling burgundy, 116, 198
Sparkling water, 21
Sparkling wine, 25, 116, 174, 199
Speegle, Paul, 154
Spelling of "whiskey," 42
Spices, 48, 77, 107, 130
"Spirit," 33
Spirit blend; *see* Blended whiskey
Spiritus frumenti, 6, 199
Spock, Dr. Benjamin, 168
Stalin, Josef, 66
Stars, 59
State Department, 110
Steam baths, 17
Steam beer, 104-105
Steam, Pat, 105
Steins, 101
Stewart, Earl D., 161
Stimulant, 128, 136–137, 147
Stirring, 11, 23, 74, 77, 152
Stock ale, 105
"Stolen" liquor, 36
Stomach, 10, 14, 15, 17, 20, 22, 26, 89, 119, 133, 134, 135, 143; absorption from, 15, 17, 20; upset, 10, 14, 26, 143
"Stone Wall," 48
Stout, 5, 86, 88, 105–106
"Straight," 3, 12, 45, 50, 51, 58, 147–149; brandy, 58; whiskey, 3, 12, 45, 50, 51, 147–149
Strength of drinkers, 126, 127
Strengths of drinks; *see* Alcoholic contents
Stress, 83, 90–92, 118–119, 139
Strip stamp, 36
Suburbanites, 151
Sugar, 21, 26, 27, 51, 55, 61, 73, 78, 79, 81, 84, 117, 125, 135, 159, 161; allergy, 135; blood-sugar level, 26, 27, 73; sugared wines, 117
Sunlight, 18, 102–103, 115, 126
Sunstroke, 136–137
Sweden, 61
Sweet mixes, 72, 134, 160
Switzerland, 57, 81, 111
Swizzles, 60, 77, 199
Sykes scale, 39
Sylvius, Professor, 56
Symposium, 6

Table wines, 25, 73, 108, 114, 115, 116, 119, 122, 157, 160, 161, 199
"Tall one," 11
Tap equipment, beer, 102, 104
Taro, 70
Tarrytown, N. Y., 74
Tartars, 6
Taste, as motive, 8
Taxes, 34, 36, 49, 50, 56, 67, 74, 87, 88, 94, 107, 116, 121, 177
Teetotalers, 4, 16, 167, 182–183, 199; number increasing, 4, 182–183
Temperatures: beer serving, 100; wine serving, 110
Tennessee, 178, 187, 188
Tension, 7, 19, 27, 90–92, 118–119, 127, 129, 159
Tenth; *see* Bottles
Tequila, 69–70, 107, 161; tequila Martini, 70
Texas, 164, 174, 187, 188
Therapeutic values, 7, 16, 79, 119, 126, 129, 138
Thirst, 10, 64, 84, 90, 93–94, 134, 143–144, 146
Thomas, "Professor" Jerry, 75
Throat, 14, 72
Thujone, 81–82
Timothy, 119
Toasting, 69, 199
Tobacco, 5, 125, 131, 136
Toddy, 6, 61, 138
Tokay, 114, 199
Tolerance for alcohol, 25–27, 30, 131, 133, 135; decrease of, 133; increasing, 25–26; low, 26, 135
Tom and Jerry, 61, 75, 77
Tomatoes, fermented, 6
Tom Collins, 55, 161
Tonics, 4
Torpedo juice, 6
Traditions, 46, 47, 48
Tranquilizers, 7, 12, 92, 129, 132, 164
Tranquilizing effects, 7, 16, 90–92, 118–120, 129; of beer, 90–92; of wine, 118–119
Toulouse-Lautrec, 81
Trinidad rum; *see* Rum
Truffles, 130
Tufts University, 167
Turkish baths, 145
Typists, 127

Uganda, 106
Uisge beatha, 48
Ulcers, 73, 139
Ullman, Dr. Albert, 167
Unadvertised brands, 34
Unconsciousness, 29
Unions, 85, 138
United Nations Building, 176
United States Brewers Academy, 98
University of California, 98, 110, 138, 161, 184
University of Chicago, 89
University of Indiana, 22
University of Mississippi, 177
"U.P.," 39
Urine, alcohol in, 17
Utah, 163, 165, 187, 189

Vanilla, 41
Vanilla extract, 4
Vegetable coloring, 80
Vermont, 188
Vermouth, 11, 12, 21, 23, 25, 55, 75, 76, 78, 113, 116, 130, 133, 151, 153, 154; alco-

holic contents, 21, 25; blandness trend, 113
Vernon, Admiral, 61–62
Veterinarians, 130
Vinegar, 125
"Vintage," 114–115
Virginia, 174, 176, 187, 189
Virgin Islands rum; *see* Rum
Vision, 16, 30, 127
Vitamins, 102, 140, 146, 158; balance with calories required, 140; beer, 102, 158; wine, 158
Vivacious people, 26
Vodka, 5, 12, 22, 25, 32, 41, 62–69, 76, 81, 118, 122, 133, 136, 148, 157, 160, 161, 163, 164, 200; alcoholic contents, 22, 62, 66; blendability of, 65; calories in, 157, 160, 161; charcoal-filtered, 63; diluted alcohol, 62–63, 67; effects of, 118, 133; flavored vodkas, 200; popularity of, 62–66; Russian, 22, 122
Voice, 14
V.S.O., 59, 200
V.V.S.O.P., 59, 200

Wahl-Henius Institute of Brewing, 100
Walking, 17, 145
Washington Alcohol Problems Association, 180
Washington, D. C., 20, 174, 176, 197, 189
Washington, George, 48–49, 74, 97
Washington, Martha, 97
Washington, State of, 175, 180, 188
Washington State Temperance Association, 180
Water, 11, 33, 36, 47, 49–50, 54, 62, 67, 84, 99, 142, 146; addicts to, 142; in beer, 84, 99; for distilling, 47, 49–50; spirits diluted with, 33, 36, 54, 62, 67
"Water holes," 96
Water of life, 48, 57
Water, tax on, 177
W.C.T.U., 141, 179
Weddings, 154
Weight, alcohol by, 87–88
Weinbrand, 57
Weisse mit Schuss, 106
West Virginia, 187, 189
"Wet Martini," 76
Wheat, 106, 135; allergy, 135; wheat beer, 106
Whiskey, 3, 5, 12, 21, 24–25, 30, 31, 33–35, 37–38, 40–53, 109, 126–127, 133, 134, 147–149, 160–161; aging, 50, 53; alcoholic contents, 15, 21, 24–25, 30, 31; bad, 40; blended, 3, 41, 42, 43, 44–46, 50, 147–149; bonded, 25, 50, 51–52, 58, 134, 160; bourbon (*see* Bourbon); brokers, 35; calories in, 157, 160, 161; Canadian (*see* Canadian whiskey); charcoal-mellowed, 190; cheap, 34, 35; Chinese, 70; corn, 5, 37–38, 41, 42, 49, 92, 135; effects of, 24, 126–127, 133, 134, 147–149; "good," 40–41; grain, 45–46, 48, 134; Highland whisky, 47; how made, 33, 41, 50; imitation whiskey, 37; "instant whiskey," 48; Irish, 41, 42, 48, 51, 53, 130; origin of, 48; prices, 12; rye (*see* Rye); Scotch (*see* Scotch whisky); spelling of, 42; straight, 3, 12, 45, 50, 51, 58, 147–149; wine in, 50, 109
Whiskey sour, 198
Whiskey Blanc, 69
Whiskey plant, 6
Whiskey Rebellion, 48–49
Whisper Martini, 75
White Lightning, 37–38
Wichita Falls, Texas, 164
Wilde, Oscar, 167
Wine, age of, 113–114; alcoholic contents, 4, 25, 28, 29, 30, 32, 116, 119; apéritif, 116; apple, 109; bargains, 115; blackberry, 109; Cabernet, 13, 190; California, 109, 114; calories in, 157, 159–161; care of, 115; celery, 109; Chardonnay, 190; claret, 119, 157, 191; currant, 109; dandelion, 109; "dessert," 25, 108, 161, 192; effects of, 14, 118, 119, 120, 134, 139; elderberry, 25; estate bottled, 115, 192; favored in Russia, 122; flavor revolution, 116–117; flavors, 116; Gamay, 112, 113; homemade, 98, 109; imported, 110–112; kosher, 117; madeira, 114, 195; marsala, 195; mulled, 138; nomenclature, 108, 111–112, 116; Palomino, 112; parsnip, 109; perishable, 114–115; Pinot Blanc, 196; Pinot Noir, 13, 112, 196; port, 25, 111, 112, 114, 119, 139, 197; prices, 13, 111, 114, 115, 120; in prison, 6; rape, 109; rhubarb, 109; ritual, 108, 110; rosé, 114, 197; in rum, 60, 109; sauterne, 111–112, 198; Sauvignon Blanc, 112, 198; Semillon, 112, 198; sherry, 13, 19, 51, 57–58, 60, 111, 112, 114, 162, 198; sparkling, 25, 112, 116, 174, 199; "special natural," 116; "table," 25, 73, 108, 114–116, 119, 122, 157, 160–161, 199; tokay, 114, 199; tranquilizing effect, 118–119; "varietal," 111–112; after whiskey, 11; in whiskey, 50, 109; *see also* Appendix
Wine and Food Society, 70, 109
Wine Appreciation Course, 110
Wine as Food and Medicine, 119
Wineglass, 75, 200
Wineries, 115
"Winos," 120
Wisconsin, 71, 175, 176, 188; brandy in, 71
Women, 66, 93, 131–132, 182–183; abstainers, 183; alcohol tolerance of, 131; drinking by, 182–183; influence of, 66, 93, 183
Wonder drug, 16
Wood alcohol; *see* Methyl alcohol
Wood chips, 37
World War II, 6, 39, 54, 85, 121
Wormwood, 81–82; wormwood tea, 82
Worries, 16, 120, 128
Wyoming, 187, 189

Yale University, 18, 82, 90, 96, 118, 127, 129
Yeast, 6, 86, 94, 97
Yellow gin, 54
Yohimbime, 130

Zombie, 61
Zubrowka, 65